D1572039

# The Tell-Tale Eye

# The Tell-Tale Eye

## HOW YOUR EYES REVEAL HIDDEN THOUGHTS AND EMOTIONS

**ECKHARD H. HESS**
**The University of Chicago**

 **Van Nostrand Reinhold Company**
*New York/Cincinnati/Toronto/London/Melbourne*

Van Nostrand Reinhold Company Regional Offices:
New York  Cincinnati  Chicago  Millbrae  Dallas

Van Nostrand Reinhold Company International Offices:
London      Toronto      Melbourne

Library of Congress Catalog Card Number: 74-29309
ISBN: 0-442-23390-6

Manufactured in the United States of America

Published by Van Nostrand Reinhold Company
450 West 33rd Street, New York, N.Y.   10001

Published simultaneously in Canada by Van Nostrand Reinhold Ltd.

15 14 13 12 11 10 9 8 7 6 5 4 3 2 1

Library of Congress Cataloging in Publication Data

Hess, Eckhard Heinrich, 1916–
    The tell-tale eye.

    Bibliography: p.
    Includes index.
    1. Pupillometrics.  I. Title.  [DNLM:  1. Eye.
2.  Nonverbal communication.   HM258 H586t]
QP360.H47        612'.84        74-29309
ISBN 0-442-23390-6

*to my wife, Dorle,*
*who made it all possible*

LOOK INTO A PERSON'S PUPILS,
HE CANNOT HIDE HIMSELF.

Confucius, 551–478 B.C.

# Preface

"Window to the Soul" was the title of this book when I wrote the first draft. Between then and now I have had a number of suggestions for other titles. "Window to the Mind" was one, "The Eye Pupil" another, and even "What the Eyes Can Tell You." Personally I had a favorite, though somewhat clumsy, title. It was "With Gun and Camera Through the Window of the Soul." Perhaps it is still an appropriate subtitle, as the reader may discover in the following pages. But the title I finally chose is probably the most logical. The eye, more than any other part of the body can tell others something about you. The physician looks into your eye with an ophthalmoscope not only to check your eye but because by that means, he can see the progress of your hardening arteries or the signs of kidney damage. The ageing woman cannot hide her passing years because her pupils give her away. The poker player cannot hide his emotion when he draws to an inside straight and a shrewd merchant can see in his customer's pupils which item for sale is of greatest interest to him. For all these reasons, as the reader will see, I call this book *The Tell-Tale Eye.*

There were many who helped in my search for answers to the riddles which the pupil presents. Dr. James Polt, while he was my student, perhaps helped the most. He was my right hand not only through the years of academic research but during the years in which I was associated with Interpublic. We coauthored the first paper in pupillometrics in 1960 and he worked with me until 1967. Three other students took their doctorate with me in pupil research. Niles Bernick, Benjamin Beck and Alan Seltzer helped in many ways. In more recent years Slobodan Petrovich took over where Jim Polt left off. Patrick Shrout, Paul Beaver and Spero Metalis are assisting in my current pupil research in addition to carrying out work of their own. In regard to my association with the advertising and marketing world I owe a debt to Hans Zeisel who introduced me to Marion Harper, Jr. of Interpublic. In particular it was Harper and Russell Schneider of that organization who made it possible for me to explore the fascinating problems of pupillometrics in relation to advertising and marketing. The generous fee I received for my consulting supported my academic pupil research and the doctoral research of my students.

As will be clear when I discuss the beginning of my pupil research, I owe an enormous debt to my wife Dorle. Not only did she give me the starting idea but helped so much when the going was rough. I also thank the University of Chicago for supplying the space in which I could carry out some of the research described.

I owe a debt also to Dorothy Ford who typed the first and the last draft of this manuscript, and to Dr. Elizabeth Goodwin who checked out the references and took care of the many details involved in getting permission for illustrations and so on. I also wish to acknowledge the efforts of George Narita in urging me to complete this manuscript, the very great aid I received from Rachel Davison and Alberta Gordon, and Ellen Trager who edited the final copy. But particularly I am indebted to David Popoff of the *Scientific American* editorial staff. When I needed help in the final editing he graciously spent a day with me. What he did, more than point out the problems of the manuscript and some solutions, was to give me an appreciation of the creative joys that can be involved in editing. For that I will always be grateful.

ECKHARD H. HESS

# Contents

# The Tell-Tale Eye

# Introduction

These lovely lamps, these windows of the soul.

> Guillaume de Salluste du Bartas (1544–1590).
> *Divine Weekes and Workes.* First Week, Sixth Day.

There is probably no part of the human body other than the human eye where I feel so intuitively that we have access to the innermost workings of the mind. This book is about the human eye and in particular, about the pupil of the eye. I will not attempt to explain its physiological or neurological workings; indeed, no one really has this precise and complete information. Instead, I want to take you on a trip to follow a research project which began fifteen years ago.

Almost everyone has ideas about eyes, and adjectives have been ascribed to the eyes in great profusion. Words like soft, hard, beady, tiny, large, saucer-like, hateful, sly, doe-like, shifty, crafty, wide, narrow, cold, warm, passionate, fiery, loving, listless, lively, shining, dull, sparkling, curious, and a host of others have been applied to the eyes to indicate mood or character. While such usage has been carried out rather unscientifically, there is now an increasing scientific recognition of the fact that a person's eyes, or, more specifically, his pupils, actually do furnish an objective index of his emotional and mental activity. Even in the older literature, for example, in medieval poetry, we find mention of the fact that the pupils grow "large with love" when an individual looks into the eyes of another appropriate individual. One can often find sentences by authors which indicate quite clearly that this phenomenon has been observed for a great

3

many years. For example, one writer may use the term "his eyes were pinpoints of hate." Another author may say "her pupils grew dark as she looked," and this is, of course, an obvious reference to the fact that the pupils increased in size.

In quite another context, I came across a passage in a book by Richard Gump in which he described his early experiences as a jade buyer for Gump's of San Francisco in the early part of this century. He went to China and learned the details and intricacies of buying jade objects from a man named Newell. Gump wrote

It was harder to learn to disguise his natural joy upon examining a beautiful object. The Chinese were aware that the pupils of the eyes dilated when one's interest was aroused and acted accordingly. Newell had earlier solved this problem by wearing dark glasses.

A similar report has come from Turkey describing how rug merchants sold rugs to Europeans.

Almost everyone knows that more light, a sensory stimulation, causes pupils to grow smaller and that less light makes them become larger. It is also generally known that terror or fright will cause the pupils to enlarge. Both these phenomena have been known in scientific circles for many years, and a great deal of work has been done, particularly on the effect of light and dark stimulation on the pupil of the eye. But the effect of milder degrees of emotion, interest, or mental activity has not been studied to the same degree, and this is largely what we will be talking about in this book. There are obviously other causes for changes in pupil size. When we try to focus our eye on something close by our pupils get smaller. This is the result of accommodation of the lenses to the shorter focusing distance. Pain causes the pupil to enlarge and so do certain types of drugs. In addition, it is possible to find changes in pupil size which are the result of brain damage. Some of the workers in the field of pupillography have found that when properly measured, differences in pupil size between the two eyes can give a fairly good indication of the location of damage in certain parts of the brain.

What I particularly want to stress is that the pupil of the eye is intimately connected to all parts of the brain, and as a result, we have the anomalous situation of having a piece of the brain sticking out of the human body for all the world to see and to evaluate.

I not only want to take the reader through some of the scientific results of our work but also to let him see some of the problems that often confront the scientist when he embarks on a project which may go into unexplored areas. In this regard, then, the book is not only an account of some research results but also a personal statement of the joys and frustrations that are a real part of the day to day experiences in the life of a scientist.

# 2

# How It Began

One night in bed about fifteen years ago I was leafing through a book of strikingly beautiful animal photographs. My wife, who was also sitting and reading in bed, happened to glance over at me and remark that the light must be bad because my pupils were unusually large. She might be more apt to notice this because she paints portraits of people and the size of pupils is of consequence in depicting individuals. I assured my wife that I had plenty of light. I had it coming over my left shoulder the way I had learned in school, and I continued to look at the book. A few minutes later she looked at me again and said that certainly I couldn't have enough light because my pupils were unusually large. I thought that this was worth checking into, so I went over to the bathroom and looked in the mirror where I noticed that my eyes seemed to be just about right for the amount of light that was falling on them at that time. I returned to bed but I thought that possibly there was a problem with the light and decided that it was time to go to sleep. However, I found it very difficult to sleep; something was nagging me. I thought of the possible reasons for having large pupils, light being of course the obvious one, but I excluded this. As a psychologist I of course knew that strong emotional stimuli, mentioned by many people including Charles Darwin, would cause the pupil of the eye to increase. This did not seem to be the case for the situation since I was looking at pictures which to me were esthetically pleasing. I continued to be bothered by this, found it difficult to sleep and rose very early in the morning to get to the laboratory. When I arrived, there was as yet no one present. I looked around for some photographs because I had an idea for a very simple experiment that I was going to try on the first person who entered my office. I found a number of 8 x 10 photographs of landscapes and a picture of a pinup. They were essentially identical in that they were all black and white 8 x 10 photographs. I placed them in an order such that I was not certain where the pinup was located in the sequence, and then waited. Dr. James Polt, who at that time was my research assistant, came early and I asked him to come and sit down and be a subject for the first of what was to be a long series of experiments. I put the photographs face down so that I could not see which one I was holding up and one at a time showed them to Dr. Polt in a position which was just over my forehead. I asked him to look at the pictures as I showed them to him one by one. He was not very far from me and since he has light blue eyes it was very easy to see his pupils. I showed the pictures to him for a few seconds each and when I came to the seventh picture I noticed a distinct increase in his pupils. I turned the picture over and, sure enough, it was the pinup—the picture I had included in the series of photographs with the calculation that it might be more interesting than the rather dull landscapes which I had also shown. Of course this is not an experiment in the usual scientific sense. However, it seemed quite reasonable to me that we should develop a procedure which would give us a much clearer indication of the changes and perhaps a way of measuring them so that they could be quantified.

Dr. Polt and I then discussed the best and simplest way of starting our research. We obtained a number of photographs which we then made up into slides. These were 2 x 2 Kodachromes which we mounted into a projector. We also made up a number of slides which we called control slides. These control slides were of approximately the same brightness as the picture which would follow. We wanted to try to be as sure as we could that any change in pupil size would not be due to the brightness of the picture but rather to some sort of intrinsic interest that the picture might have. We had difficulty in getting exact equality but we did the best we could. Then, we hit upon a very simple solution to our problem. Why, we argued, could we not use different kinds of subjects, assuming in a common sense fashion,

**Figure 1** Pictures of appealing babies normally elicit strong pupil dilation responses in women but not in men. Young children also have been found to respond with marked pupil dilation to pictures of babies.

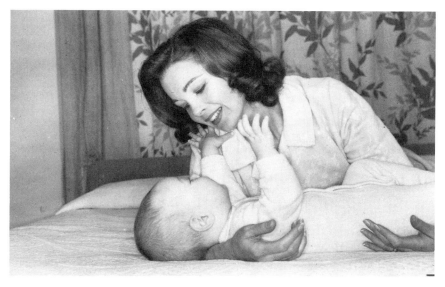

**Figure 2** Women usually have strong pupil dilation responses to pictures of mothers with babies. Men generally have pupil dilation responses to such pictures but these responses are directed toward the mother and not the child.

**Figure 3**   Pictures of nude men produce strong pupil dilation responses in normal women, but not usually in heterosexual men. Homosexual men, however, show pupil dilation responses to some pictures of nude men. Data obtained from homosexual subjects show that certain kinds of pictures of men have much stronger homosexual appeal than do others. (From Ruby, Erik A., *The Human Figure: A Photographic Guide for Artists.* Van Nostrand Reinhold Company, New York, 1974.)

that men would have different interests in what they look at than would women? We selected five photographs. The first was a picture of a baby; the second, a picture of a mother and a baby; the third, a picture of a nude man; the fourth, a pinup; and the last, a picture of a landscape. We thought that we might get differences in the way the first four pictures would interest men and women but expected to have the response to the landscape to be about the same for both. We made what I was later told by "experts" to be a naïve assumption, which was that women might prefer to look at a picture of a man rather than a picture of a woman. I also had in the back of my mind the notion that a

**Figure 4** Female pinup pictures cause normal heterosexual men to respond with strong pupil dilation, while heterosexual women show little or no pupil dilation responses. Homosexual men tend not to show pupil dilation or pupil constriction to female pinup pictures. (From Ruby, Erik A., *The Human Figure: A Photographic Guide for Artists.* Van Nostrand Reinhold Company, New York, 1974.)

**Figure 5** Landscapes usually evoke small pupil size changes of either constriction or dilation. Landscape scenes are often used in our pupil research to provide affectively neutral pictorial stimuli. They are used particularly at the beginning of a series of slides, so that the important pictures are not subject to the "first picture effect" that we have found. The "first picture effect" refers to the fact that the first picture in a series usually causes pupil dilation responses because of its novelty.

picture of a baby might be more interesting to women than it might be to men. This is partly because babyishness seems to have rather universal appeal but apparently more so to women than to men. We will talk more about this later in the book. We made a crude apparatus in which it was possible to photograph the eye at the rate of two pictures per second while the subject was looking at photographs which were projected on a translucent screen from its rear. In this way the subject had an unobstructed view of the pictures. We then began to test a number of people. Each subject was asked to sit comfortably and to look for ten seconds at a control slide with the numbers 1, 2, 3, 4, 5 as in Figure 6. Following each control slide he was allowed to look as he wished at one of the five pictures, in each case for a period of ten seconds. After we had tested a few men and women we had the film processed. We measured it by rear-projecting the film on a translucent surface and measuring the pupil sizes, as shown in 20 enlarged photographs for each ten seconds of looking, with a millimeter scale. We then tabulated our results. By taking the average pupil size in area for the ten seconds of looking at a control slide and then the average pupil size for the ten seconds of looking at a picture, we soon arrived at a score of per cent change in pupil area for each individual for each picture. The results were astonishing. Even with such unstimulating materials as in our first test, we obtained results that very clearly differentiated the men from the women subjects. The results are shown in Figure 7 and indicate very plainly the sex differences in the amount of interest value these various photographs had. The response for the men as far as the baby was concerned was essentially zero. The women, on the other hand, had a very good response. In the case of the mother and child the women had the largest pupil dilation and we have found in subsequent experiments that there seems to be something rather appealing or interesting to women in looking at a picture of a mother and a baby. The men had a slight increase which was, however, not significant. But the nicest difference, at least because it conformed with our earlier expectations and hopes, was the difference between men and women in the way they viewed the nude man and nude woman. The results in each case were exactly the opposite for the two sexes.

The smallest difference between men and women was for the picture of the landscape. In fact, the women, while looking at this rather drab, uninteresting scene, actually had a slight pupil constriction; that is, the pupils were smaller when they were looking at the picture of the landscape than they were when they were looking at the control slide which just preceded it. Although we did not use many subjects, the results were so appealing that ideas by the dozen came to us for other kinds of experiments we might carry out. We thought the best thing to do would be to write up this rather brief experiment and publish it in a journal so that many people would get to know about it and the potential research opportunities. We chose to send the paper to *Science*, the official journal of the American Association for

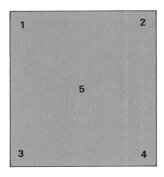

**Figure 6**   Control slides used in our pupillometric research are made up like the one in this figure. Control slides are shown between each stimulus slide in a series. They are matched in overall average brightness to the specific stimulus slide that they precede.

the Advancement of Science. However, once having written the paper I began to worry that perhaps material of this sort had been published previously. To now publish it as an original finding which could open up interesting areas of research might be an unfortunate mistake. There are many instances in which someone who has published a discovery finds that it had actually been discovered before.

In fact, a very interesting case of this sort is that of seeing colors when certain black and white patterns are rapidly spun around. These are called "subjective colors" because they are not actually produced by specific wavelengths but are the *subjective* experience of the person who looks at them. This phenomenon of "subjective color," has been discovered and rediscovered a total of sixteen times in the literature covering a span of almost 200 years. This happens much more frequently than should be the case, perhaps because of the fantastic and mountainous volume of publications which is produced in this world so that not as much of it is read by any individual worker in the field as might have been the case some time ago. At any rate I decided to hold off a bit and ask two of my research assistants to help me survey the literature to see what we could find. My problem was solved much more simply because somewhat later on the street while on my way to the laboratory, I came across one of our distinguished faculty members at the University of Chicago, Dr. Heinrich Klüver. Dr. Klüver is a man of tremendous knowledge as far as scientific literature, particularly of vision, is concerned. After describing the experiment we had just done and written up, I asked him whether he knew of something of this sort as being part of the previously published literature. He thought a few

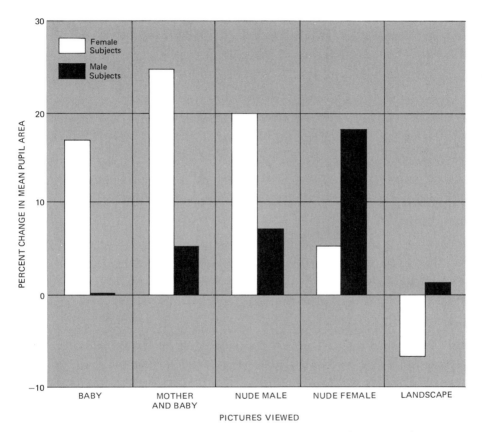

**Figure 7**    Depicted are the pupil responses of the men and women subjects to the five pictures studied in our original 1960 pilot investigation that was reported in *Science*. The changes in pupil size are shown in terms of the average decrease or increase in area during the viewing of each picture, in comparison with the area during the viewing of the control slides. The white bars show that the two women had different pupil responses to different pictures, while the black bars show that the four men had a different pattern of pupil responses to the pictures. The different pupil response patterns shown by the men and women indicate that their pupil responses were not solely dependent upon light intensity since they all looked at the same series of pictures.

seconds, and said, "Well, there was, of course, some work by Bumke," and he gave me the approximate reference and mentioned one or two other people. But finally he said, no, this seemed to him to be sufficiently different because what we were dealing with was a sensitivity in relation to very subtle differences in interest that might be evinced by people. I wasted no time getting to the laboratory, got out the manuscript, and mailed it off to *Science*. It was published within a matter of weeks, which is a tremendously short publication lag—the usual sequence being that one does a study, writes a paper, and then it may be in some instances a year, a year and a half, sometimes two years before the paper actually appears in print in a journal. I then waited to hear from other researchers about our work because it obviously seemed to me to offer possibilities in a great many ways. However, almost nothing happened in the way of communications from the scientific community. What did happen, instead, was that the article was picked up by one of the press associations and reports of it appeared in hundreds of newspapers in the United States. A local Chicago paper which had interviewed me for additional information discussed the research with the headline "Scientist's Wife Provides Clue to the Cheesecake-Photo Effect." This headline greatly appealed to my wife who referred to me for weeks afterwards as "Scientist's Wife's Husband," a phrase which I thought only slightly amusing.

Sometime later I received notification of the first pupil colloquium which was to be held at the Massachusetts Institute of Technology. Apparently my invitation came as a result of the paper I had published in *Science*. Although the majority of the pupil workers who were listed in the invitation dealt with pupil changes in relation to light and neurological mechanisms, I thought this would be a wonderful opportunity to bring up the research, discuss it, and perhaps get ideas and contribute suggestions for further work. I therefore went to the conference in high spirits. The group was not large, consisting of a few dozen individuals. I presented my material for about a half-hour with continually decreasing enthusiasm because I noted that the expressions on the faces of the people to whom I was talking were by no means supportive. In fact, most of the faces looked downright unfriendly. When I finished there was a short period of silence. Then the Dean of the pupillographers, the late Dr. Otto Löwenstein, got up, addressed me as "young man" and proceeded to tell me I had no business working in this area since I really didn't understand all the intricacies of how the pupil worked. To say that I was taken aback would be putting it mildly. I was tempted to say that neither did anyone else in the room understand how the pupil worked but I was sufficiently depressed by this attitude that I felt it rather useless to engage in a discussion. I did make one suggestion, however. I pointed out that several of the individuals had pupillometers, that is, instruments which allowed the automatic recording of changes of the pupil as a subject sat in a fixed position. It would therefore be very simple for them to try something of the sort that I just described and see for themselves that the results I had described could be obtained. One of the researchers then got up and gave me the classic nonsense answer that a scientist can give. It was, "I don't have to try it. I know it doesn't work." That put the finishing touches on my general feeling for the day and I remember sitting in the Boston hotel room that evening instead of going out to dinner, feeling very sorry for myself. However, by morning the world seemed brighter and my head again was full of ideas that I wanted very badly to try as soon as I got back to my laboratory in Chicago. There, we began a series of studies and many of them we did not treat exhaustively. We just wanted to find out whether or not something would work and get answers for ourselves. With joy and enthusiasm we tried almost everything and some of these experiments will be described later in this book.

Slowly, but surely, over several years, the interest of other scientists began to show itself. We had many visitors to our laboratory, some of them staying as much as a week. They came to find out how our technique worked and to get information on equipment and procedure. We gave freely of this information and advice. Some of those we wined, dined, and informed with no tremendous enthusiasm because it seemed clear that their main objective was to do what is somewhat fashionable in a certain segment of the scientific population. Having few ideas of their own, their one chance to get ahead in the world is to latch on to someone else's work, repeat the experiment or experiments with some small changes and come out with different results which can then be published under "negative findings."

As a matter of fact, in some instances the entire reputation of a scientist may be built upon a cornerstone which consists of a repetition of a classic experiment with negative results. In many cases, of course, it turns out later that the differences in the procedure and technique are responsible for the differences in findings but this is not then published. It is a little bit like an attack on someone in the press which is printed on page one and sometime later there is a retraction on page sixteen. The difficulty is that the damage has been done.

However, I console myself with the fact that in time things generally work out. A famous European psychologist, Otto Köhler, once said that every time one makes a real discovery or opens up a new field of research the process goes through three stages. First, upon publication the work is ignored. Sometime later there is a period in which a number of repetitions by other scientists are made and the finding is shown to be "incorrect." And then finally when the mass of evidence really does accumulate it is treated as though this is something that everyone had known all along. This experience was not new to me. About twenty years ago I published some work on the effects of very early experience in young animals and described a critical period in which certain experiences are extremely effective in producing certain kinds of behavior changes. This phenomenon is called *imprinting*. For some years after publication the work was ignored. Then there was a period of years during which the proposition I had propounded was under attack by almost all workers in the general area of animal behavior and particularly those who had to do with developmental aspects of young organisms. Now, however, the final phase has been reached and the material is to be found in nearly every psychology textbook, and usually when it is referred to by these scientists in other papers it is taken for granted as having been known all along.

If that timetable is any precedent for what is happening now with my pupil research we are obviously in stage two; that is, many people are finding it useful to get negative results. But, it is a happy thing for me to see that there are also very many papers which are coming out in corroboration with some of the research findings that I have published during the past several years.

At any rate, as I have said earlier, we have had many scientists visit our laboratory. We have helped many of them, and there are now dozens of researchers using this tool in a great variety of research areas ranging from strictly experimental psychology to social psychology, psychiatry and psychotherapy, all the way to advertising and marketing. Work directly involving the experimental findings which we have made is going on at a great many research institutions and universities as well as in the industrial and marketing fields.

While the methods, techniques and equipment we use are essentially cumbersome and expensive, this does not have to be the case. The actual pupil changes are so easily observed that one can, with reasonable success, create and watch the pupil changes in another individual simply by showing him a series of pictures, much in the same way that I did in my first test with Dr. Polt. Some of the many letters I have received have been from high school students who wanted to enter Science Fair projects. I have given them advice as to how it might be possible for a high school student who has access to an inexpensive motion picture camera and a slide projector, to carry out pupillometric research. The motion picture camera should have a single frame device, that is, a button which when pushed exposes a single frame on the film. With the right illumination and very fast black and white motion picture film, it is possible to obtain photographs of the pupil. With this method it is best to use light-eyed subjects. No complicated apparatus need be used. A simple frame for holding the head can be devised; and then by means of a stand such as is used in the laboratory or even one made out of wood, the camera can be held. A mirror can be so situated that it reflects a picture of the eye, let us say in this case the left eye, to the motion picture camera which is at a right angle to the direction of the person's gaze. A small rear projection screen can be made out of a wooden frame over which thin paper is stretched and any slide projector can provide the material which is shown to the subject. Or, the screen can be used to provide a surface on which there is a fixation point at which the subject can look while he does mental arithmetic problems or other sort of mental activity. The slide projector can then again be used by inserting a glass sandwich through which the film is pulled slowly frame by frame while an assistant measures the projected pupil which can be enlarged, as we do, usually twenty or more times.

The next chapter gives a brief historical review of scientific work that has been done with the pupil. The reader may want to proceed directly to Chapter 4, where our own findings are presented, and later refer to the historical material in Chapter 3.

**3**

# A Little History

Some years ago I was visited by a writer from the *Saturday Evening Post*. His name was Bill Davidson and he proved to be a charming and astute interviewer. He was with me for several days and followed us through some of the pupil research for an article he was writing for the *Post*. Before he finished he thought that perhaps we should call this area by some name, and in the process of trying to find some sort of answer for him I coined the term *pupillometrics*. This term has stuck and it is now used by other workers in the field I am describing.

For many years the pupil of the eye has been the subject of a huge quantity of scientific research and thousands of research papers have been published. However, the psychopupil response has been discussed in only a relatively small part of this literature, since many of the other papers deal with the mechanisms of pupil change, the way in which the iris muscles work, and so forth. Such research work has been called *pupillography,* another reason that the term *pupillometrics* is a good one for referring to work dealing with the psychopupil response.

After the turn of the century a German neuropsychiatrist at Freiburg, Oswald Bumke, wrote a book about the pupil's movement in normal people and in those having neurological and mental diseases. This book was a summary of what was known at that time about pupillary activity. Bumke made the point that as far as normal people were concerned, "every active intellectual process, every psychical effort, every exertion of attention, every active mental image, regardless of content, particularly every affect just as truly produces pupil enlargement as does every sensory stimulus . . ." That is, not only does the perception of the world about us influence the size of the pupil, but also every mental and emotional response to this world. Bumke pointed out, for example, that mentally counting the beats of a metronome will cause rhythmic pupillary dilations and contractions in time with the metronome beats and that even a moderate handshake will elicit pupil enlargement. Otto Löwenstein, another neuropsychiatrist of German origin, in 1920 reaffirmed that fact as generally known and accepted, adding that even the very beginning of "volitional impulses" or thoughts could be reflected in pupillary dilation.

However well known all these facts were in the German literature for several decades after the publication of Bumke's book, they were not very well known in this country. One reason for this was the relative isolation of many American scientists from their European counterparts, an isolation that persisted until after World War II. Another might possibly be the relatively observational nature of the supporting data. For example, the effect of doing arithmetic mentally was studied by a German, W. Heinrich. He painstakingly recorded the amount of dilation that occurred while his subjects were performing problems in their heads, but he did not tell us exactly what problems he gave his subjects to solve. Other researchers were sometimes rather casual and not very specific about stating just what it was that they did to make eye pupils dilate. For example, they sometimes limited their description of their experimental procedure to merely stating that the subjects were requested to "recall a date," or that they "gave a suggestion of fear."

Thus it was, that the experimental observations of pupillary responses to mental processes and to mild emotional states fell into relative obscurity for several decades. Only the fact that strong emotional states dilate pupils and the fact that abnormal bodily states such as being under the influence of narcotic drugs will produce abnormalities in pupillary activity appear to have been generally known during this time. Fortunately, recent efforts and investigations by scientific researchers have begun to produce more quantitative and systematic data regarding all these phenomena. As a result, the notion that most, perhaps all, mental, sensory, and emotional processes may be observed in the behavior of the eye pupil is gaining increasing acceptance among both scientists and laymen.

In 1765, observations of Felice F. Fontana, the Italian physiologist and naturalist at the University of Pisa, showed that eye pupils will dilate upon awaking from sleep even though strong light is shining in them. A hundred years later, the Berlin psychiatrist Carl F. Westphal attempted to make a systematic and thorough study of the effects of nonvisual sensory stimulation, that is, the effects of sensations that did not come through the eyes, upon pupil size. Westphal noted that when a person has been sedated with chloroform anesthesia, his eye pupils become extremely tiny. In spite of this, if the person were pricked with a needle, his eye pupils would enlarge quite noticeably. The pupils, of course, would go back to the tiny size right after the needle prick. The same momentary enlargement of eye pupils happened whenever Westphal bent down and shouted in the person's ear. However, if the person were anesthetized heavily with chloroform the eye pupils would fail to dilate in response to needle pricks or screams. Finally, Westphal also noted that the eye pupils would dilate if the person were suddenly awakened from the chloroform anesthesia.

Also in the last century, a physiologist in Germany, Moritz Schiff, concluded that pupillary size changes were an excellent measure of the sensations that a person experienced. Because he usually saw the pupil get bigger at even the merest touch when his experimental animals had been anesthetized, he called the eye pupil an "esthesiometer." There was no pain involved at all in this pupil response to such sensory stimulation. However, the amount of dilation was greater for stronger sensory stimulation such as pressure than for touch alone. This was the reason that Schiff thought that the amount of dilation caused by a sensation was a good measure of the strength of that sensation. Pio Foa, an Italian anatomist, who worked in Schiff's laboratory at one point in his career, even thought that the eye pupil served as the *best* "esthesiometer" of the body.

Charles Darwin, the English naturalist and originator of the Darwinian theory of the evolution of species, made some interesting observations upon the eyes as indicators of emotion. In his book written in 1872, *The Expression of the Emotions in*

*Man and Animals*, he mentioned the widening and narrowing of the eyes through the movements of the eyelids as correlated with emotional states in people. He also discussed the dilation of the pupil in emotional states such as fear and surprise.

Two decades later, W. Heinrich, working as a student in the physiology laboratory of Sigmund Exner in Vienna, asked four male subjects to perform "difficult" mental multiplication problems and other calculations while they were looking directly and steadily at a specific spot. Heinrich measured different amounts of pupil dilation in the different subjects, upon different occasions. These differences may perhaps have been due to differences in the ability of the four men to solve arithmetic problems in their heads and perhaps also because some of the problems they were asked to solve were more difficult than others. Heinrich reported that the diameter of his subjects' pupils increased 7, 13, 40, and 101 per cent when the arithmetic problems were being worked upon. We must be cautious in accepting these figures since there was no real instrumentation for these data.

Heinrich questioned whether changes in the focusing of the eye during the calculation of the arithmetic problems might cause the changes in the size of the eye pupil. This question came up because he found that when a subject looked far away, his pupil size was larger than when he looked nearby. So he asked one of his subjects to look steadily far away when doing the mental calculations. Although this subject's pupil diameter increased by almost half because he looked far away, his pupil grew one-quarter even larger while he was calculating.

Other effects on the pupil size were found by Heinrich during his investigations. For example, he reported that if a person was asked to pay attention to an object that he saw on the edge of his field of vision, his pupil grew larger than when he was asked to pay attention to the same object when it was in the center of his field of vision. Heinrich suggested that it was more difficult to pay attention to objects on the edge of the fields of vision than to those in the center and therefore greater effort had to be exerted in attempting to do this. This exertion of greater effort, he further suggested, caused the greater pupil size observed.

At the turn of the twentieth century a Paris physician, Jacques

Roubinovitch, made similar and independent observations on the relationship between mental processes and pupil size. He used both men and women as subjects and asked them to look constantly at a small black ball which he hung at a fixed distance from their heads. Among other things, he asked them to perform various mental tasks such as recalling a date or a name or to solve an arithmetic problem in their heads. By measuring the size of the eye pupils while these subjects were carrying out these mental tasks, Roubinovitch noticed several things. As long as the people were working on the problem they had been given, their pupils remained enlarged. At the moment that the solution to the problem was achieved, the pupils went back to the size they had been before the problem. Sometimes a person's pupil started getting larger even before Roubinovitch had finished telling him what the problem was. Roubinovitch also discovered that the pupil dilation failed to occur only when the mental task that he gave the subject was either extremely easy or else when the subject judged it to be an impossible task. As a result of these observations, Roubinovitch concluded that *both* how much the pupil enlarged and how long it was enlarged showed exactly how much intellectual effort a person was making.

There are other things besides mental effort that can result in pupil enlargement. One of them is plain and simple muscular effort such as shaking hands or lifting things.

In 1908, a Viennese neurologist Emil Redlich, and a professor of psychiatry from Bonn, Alexander Westphal both reported that contractions of the muscles to any kind of physical task, or even merely thinking about performing such physical tasks, could be counted upon to produce an enlargement of eye pupils. Later on more observations on the effects of muscular exertion on pupil size were made by Dr. Alexander Levine and a neuropsychiatrist, Dr. Paul Schilder, an Englishman, P. R. A. May in the United States, by Ronald K. Parker and Robert S. Mogyorosy of Florida State University, and Jum C. Nunnally of Vanderbilt University in Tennessee. Levine and Schilder reported that all people whose pupils respond to changes in the amount of light by appropriate changes in their size would also show the pupillary response to muscular effort. Furthermore, as Emil Redlich had earlier observed, muscular effort will cause a person's eye pupils to enlarge even when he is in very strong light, just as emotional feelings will.

At the turn of the century there was a great deal of interest in Germany in abnormalities in the pupillary behavior of mentally ill people, with or without bodily symptoms. Emil Redlich, Alexander Westphal, and Oswald Bumke all wrote extensively on this topic. Bumke's book, published in 1911, was a rather comprehensive and fascinating review of the work of a great many researchers, including himself, who had studied pupillary disturbances in psychiatric patients up to this time. These disturbances not only included special kinds of pupillary behavior among these patients but also the lack of certain pupillary phenomena which normally appear in healthy people. The range of neurological (organic) and nonorganic conditions which had been studied for pupillary processes was amazingly wide, including disorders such as meningitis, tumors of the central nervous system, polio, alcoholism, mental deficiency, addiction to opium or morphine or bromides, epilepsy, migraine, schizophrenia, wasting away of nerves controlling bodily movements, chorea (St. Vitus' Dance), and multiple sclerosis. Researchers in Russia are currently engaged in studying pupillary behavior in many of these neurological and psychiatric disorders.

One of the best known of the pupillary abnormalities described by Alexander Westphal was the "transitory catatonic pupillary abnormality" (also called "spasmus mobilis") which is found in catatonic schizophrenic patients. These are patients who keep themselves constantly in a stupor or in stereotyped rigid body positions, sometimes having periods of excitement. Westphal found that such patients have pupils that remain larger than normal and that often will fail to constrict to a flash of light or to change in size as a result of shifting focus to near or far objects. Furthermore, the pupils' response to light in the case of these patients is very changeable from moment to moment or from day to day. Not only is there sometimes a lack of response to light but also sometimes short periods of very high reactivity to light stimulation. According to the German researchers E. Meyer and Frieda Reichmann, and the American researchers Alexander Levine and Paul Schilder, this prolonged excessive dilation of the pupil has been noticed in patients having other kinds of psychiatric or neurological difficulties, including alcoholism, traumatic neurosis, syphilis, and epidemic encephalitis.

As these and other studies such as those of Otto Löwenstein have shown, this rigidly dilated pupil can easily be seen in schizophrenics whenever fear or anxiety is suggested to them and almost never happens in normal people. In fact, there was one New York doctor, Kenneth Gang, who said that this fact had been used as a bedside test to enable a physician to tell whether his patient had a catatonic stupor or was suffering from depression. Otto Löwenstein and Alexander Westphal thought that the cause of this pupillary abnormality in schizophrenics was related to their abnormal emotional expression. Schizophrenics usually are unable to control their emotions in the same way as normal people: they are extremely susceptible to heightened emotionality but at the same time are unable to be spontaneous in the expression of emotion or to recover quickly from a mild emotional disturbance. Their pupil responses occur in exactly the same way: fixed dilation, lack of response in cases where normal pupils would respond readily, and difficulty in recovering from dilation when the cause of the dilation has been removed. In normal people, in contrast, pupillary dilation will occur in response to an emotional situation, but this enlargement quickly disappears when the reason for it has been removed.

Other pupillary abnormalities which have been observed in the psychiatric population have included exaggerated constriction responses to light as reported by Löwenstein and Westphal in the case of manic-depressive psychotics when they are in the manic phase. Inequality in the size of the pupils of the two eyes is another of these observed abnormalities. The physician R. Klein and the Czechoslovakian D. F. Early published a paper in 1948 which noted that when epileptics are undergoing fits, not only do their pupils become very wide but there are also other characteristic changes in their pupil size during specific phases of the fits.

P. R. A. May, a British physician at Bexley Hospital in Kent, studied several hundred male schizophrenic patients and compared them with 100 normal males. He found that schizophrenics more often had differences in the size of the pupils of the two eyes. Almost one-fifth of them had this abnormality, in comparison with only 3 per cent of the normal men. Many of these schizophrenic men also had abnormal pupil responses to a sudden flash of light: 15 per cent had this impairment, while only 1 per cent of the normal men showed this deficiency. Furthermore, not as many of the schizophrenics showed the pupil enlargement response to pain as the normal men did. That is, only 66 per cent, or two-thirds, dilated their pupils when the skin on the back of their necks was pinched, while more than four-fifths, or 83 per cent of the normals gave this response. Similarly, when pupillary responses to muscular effort were measured, it was found that the schizophrenics were likewise deficient, for upon mild muscular effort, 61 per cent failed to dilate their pupils, while only 26 per cent of the normal men kept their pupils at the same size. When stronger, but still moderate muscular effort was required, 37 per cent of the schizophrenics still failed to enlarge their pupils, and only 15 per cent of the normal men did not dilate their pupils.

Dr. May also observed that mentally defective patients did not properly constrict their pupils to flashes of light, a fact which indicates that constitutional or acquired bodily factors play a part in these pupillary disturbances. He thought, however, that the severe emotional instability (including not being able to react to external events) of the schizophrenic patients also might be connected significantly with the higher incidences of pupillary disturbances among them. Since muscular effort has a dilating effect on pupils, muscular tension obviously does also. And changes in muscular tension, usually in the direction of increased tension, are frequently a very noticeable feature of mental and nervous disorders.

In recent years Russian neurologists and physiologists have shown a great deal of interest in the behavior of the pupil in psychiatric patients. In particular, Russian researchers have been investigating what they call the "orienting reflex," present in both humans and lower animals. One part of this "orienting reflex" is a momentary dilation of the eye pupil in response to the perception of any changes in the environment. It is a way of paying attention to and adjusting to what is about us. N. I. Streltsova, for example, studied hysteria patients. In psychiatric language, hysteria refers not just to emotional excitability or overanxious behavior, but also to the acquisition of bodily disorders such as blindness or deafness which have absolutely no actual physical basis.

At any rate, Streltsova discovered that in hysteria patients the pupillary dilation orienting reaction is considerably stronger than it is in normal persons. She thought that the underlying cause of this was in changes in the strength and reactivity of various parts of the brain, particularly its upper layer, the cortex. She also wrote that in the case of acute alcoholics, or schizophrenics, or persons suffering from epilepsy during the times they are not undergoing fits, the pupillary dilation orienting reaction is either weaker than normal or completely absent. Again, Streltsova suggested that changes in the organization of the brain were correlated with the pupillary abnormality. In this instance, however, it was inhibition of the upper levels of brain functioning that she believed were involved.

Interestingly, Streltsova also found that some medical drugs such as strychnine or caffeine will stimulate or increase the pupillary dilation orienting reflex when they are given in small doses but will inhibit its occurrence when given in larger doses. Hence it appears that physicians could easily determine proper medication and dosage for individual patients by means of observing the effects of the drugs upon the pupillary dilation reaction.

Other recent investigations have been carried out in this country. Several investigators, for example, have found that children, despite their smaller physical stature, actually have a larger pupil size than do adults. The negative correlation between absolute pupil size and age has been reported as long ago as 1896, when W. Silberkuhl of Germany presented the results of measuring the pupil sizes of adults of different ages in the same illumination condition. In moderately bright illumination young adults between 15 and 20 years of age had pupils slightly over 4 millimeters in diameter, while older adults over 50 years of age had pupils almost 3 millimeters in diameter. Adults in the age range of 20 to 50 years were found to have pupils between 3.6 millimeters and 3.1 millimeters in diameter.

Further reports of the age differential in pupil size were made in 1950, by J. E. Birren's, R. C. Casperson's, and J. Botwinick's paper in the *Journal of Gerontology,* and later by L. S. Kumnick, Leonard Rubin of the Eastern Pennsylvania Psychiatric Institute, and the psychopharmacologists Abraham Wikler, David E. Rosenberg, Jimmie D. Hawthorne, and Thomas M. Cassidy. Several hundred subjects ranging in age from 7½ to 90 years have been measured by these scientists. Although one study by Rubin and his associates, Giulio Barbero, Warren S. Chernick and Maarten S. Sibinga failed to discern any effect of age upon pupil diameter in a group of children aged from 6 to 14 years, this age difference in pupil size cannot be doubted. In a later chapter we will comment in detail upon the biological and behavioral significance of this difference in the pupil size of children and adults, particularly with respect to the survival of the human species through the care of physically helpless babies and young children.

N. I. Streltsova, the Russian investigator we mentioned earlier, also has found differences in the pupillary behavior of children and adults. She wrote that in research she had conducted in collaboration with another Russian, A. E. Liberman, there were differences in the basic regularities of the pupillary orienting reflex in accordance with age. This is congruent with the fact that Abraham Wikler and his colleagues in this country have found differences in the pupils' reaction to the drug LSD-25 according to the person's age. Streltsova also wrote that still another Russian researcher, Prikhod'ko, demonstrated various peculiarities in the pupillary orienting reflex in the case of children.

Still another population difference in pupil size has been discovered by Leonard Rubin. His data indicated that the pupil size of adults suffering from neurotic disorders is smaller than that of normal, healthy adults. While neuroses do not have any discoverable bodily basis, they can result in bodily manifestations such as tics. Neurotics do not suffer as complete a disorganization of the personality as do psychotics and thus neuroses are considered less serious than are psychoses. Neurotics are usually characterized by having anxieties, compulsions, obsessions, or groundless fears. Rubin gave further tests to his neurotic and non-neurotic subjects by having them put their hands in a bath of cold water. The neurotics and non-neurotics showed the same pupillary dilation response to this stress. Furthermore, both kinds of subjects had the same pupillary responses to light and dark illumination whether or not their hands were in the cold bath. However, when their hands were taken out of the cold water it took the neurotics longer to get their pupils back to the normal size than it did for the healthy normal subjects to do so. This phenomenon is reminiscent of the fixed pupil dilation phenomenon found in schizophrenics by Alexander Westphal.

Another study by Rubin, this time conducted together with Giulio J. Barbero and Maarten S. Sibinga, has suggested that, like the adult subjects just mentioned, children who are suffering from recurrent abdominal pain do not recover normal pupil size as well as do their normal peers when the stress is removed.

It should be pointed out that these pupillary size changes are beyond *direct* voluntary control. Otto Bumke noted that so-called voluntary pupil enlargement is invariably done *indirectly,* that is, through such means as changing focusing from near to far objects, holding the breath for several seconds, exerting enough muscular effort such as in common isometric exercises, or by inflicting pain on oneself through, say, biting the tongue. In other words, other bodily functions which in themselves can affect the size of the pupil, are used by people who believe that they can voluntarily control the size of their eye pupils. It might be added that still another way that pupil size can be indirectly increased is by calculating arithmetic problems in the head.

Recent data obtained by Lawrence M. Krueger and findings reported by Loren J. Chapman, Jean P. Chapman, and Terry Brelje indicate that either explicit instructions not to dilate pupils to pictures or the presence of an experimenter whose manner appears to have the effect of inhibiting emotional responsiveness on the part of subjects can serve to reduce somewhat the extensiveness of pupil dilation to pictures. This reduction, however, is certainly not through direct control of pupil size. William R. Clark and David A. Johnson have investigated the effects of actually instructing subjects (either correctly or erroneously) regarding the nature of pupillary dilations to be expected as the result of mental effort. The pupil responses of both subjects given correct and incorrect information regarding pupillary phenomena were not significantly different from those of a control group that had not been given any instructional set.

Hence this experiment did not demonstrate any material effect of prior instruction upon pupillary responses.

While this brief review of past investigations of the pupil response has shown that there is a very wide range of causes for pupil size change, I will deal with the psychological factors involved. This is the area I call pupillometrics.

4

# What We Have Found

In the ensuing years we did many things. First, almost immediately after publishing the paper in *Science*, we repeated the test using the same pictures to see whether or not these findings which had already been reported would really hold up. They did. In the process of testing other pictures, however, we came across a greater number of constrictions than we had anticipated. In every case these constrictions seemed to me to be responses to pictures that I would "guess" to be negative or distasteful to individuals. While I realized that obviously I cannot make judgments about how other individuals feel, in those instances where I served as the subject for a pupil experiment I found pictures that were distasteful to me produced pupil responses, which when later measured, turned out to be constrictions. This, then, opened up a completely new aspect of the work, because we had possible means of getting positive *and negative* evaluations of stimuli. If this were indeed true it would be the first known case where an autonomic response was able to go in two directions and indicate such differences of emotional interests or attitudes.

To state it simply, the initial findings seemed to indicate that when people looked at something they liked, or found appealing or interesting, their pupils would get bigger. When people looked at something they found to be uninteresting, distasteful, or negative, their pupils would get smaller. This notion has such an obvious charm that we set about testing it. We immediately made a mistake. I assumed that since I do not care to look at pictures involving accidents, mutilation, or abnormalities, this would of course provide us with precisely the useful stimulus material to get negative responses. I was wrong. There was one particular photograph, for example, of a mutilated soldier lying on a battlefield which gave us results ranging all the way from a good constriction to a reasonably high dilation. Only then did it occur to me that it might be true that the human response to, say, an accident is not always a negative one. If people really do not wish to see the mutilated victim of an accident, then there should be no gathering of crowds at places where such unfortunate incidents occur. Unfortunately this appears not to be true. In fact, one just has to look at the current popularity of violence on motion picture and television screens.

As a result, we tested a variety of photographs which we assumed to be negative. We found that mildly negative material produced reasonably consistent pupil constrictions in almost all individuals tested. An example of such a picture is one of a cross-eyed child. It is interesting to note that we get a greater negative response from women to this picture than we get from men and perhaps this is no surprise to the reader. At any rate we were off and running with this concept after we had done our initial research. This particular finding has become the basis of most of the research papers attacking pupillometrics.

Indeed, the noted pupillographer, Irene E. Loewenfeld, has stated with complete finality and authority that "all psychologic and sensory stimuli, with the exception of light dilate the pupil and none of them contract it." Among the psychologists who embrace Irene Loewenfeld's notion with complete enthusiasm are Michel Pierre Janisse of Winnipeg, Canada, and Gad Hakerem of New York. This statement can be immediately disproven. Ben Beck's thesis research done in my laboratory demonstrated that some people have pupil *constriction* responses to certain auditory stimuli. That is, some of his subjects would respond with smaller pupil sizes when they heard clicks at certain rates than when there was silence.

In addition, another study done by students in my laboratory used baby cries as stimuli and some people's pupils contracted to the cry of a baby suffering pain. In both auditory studies, there were no visual illumination changes whatever. Furthermore, pupil studies both in my laboratory and in Daniel Kahneman's laboratory at the University of Michigan, in which hypnosis was used to induce a specific attitude, have obtained pupil constriction responses.

Another fact which disproves Loewenfeld's position is that the process of hypnotic induction itself produces pupil constriction. There is, of course, no change in illumination conditions involved. Not only have we observed this in our own laboratory but professional medical hypnotists have told me that pupil constriction serves as the indication by which they know that the person is actually "going under." Since the verbal instructions during hypnotic induction may be considered a stimulus, it is clearly a stimulus that elicits pupil constriction, not dilation.

It is unquestionably more difficult for experimenters to obtain psychosensory pupil constrictions than psychosensory pupil dilations, particularly when dealing with pooled data rather than with responses of individual subjects. Consequently, many other investigators have disagreed with the entire notion of psychosensory pupil constrictions while some others have reported research demonstrating their existence. As for my own research, the facts still seem to stand.

## WORDS

Shortly after we began our work relating to the presentation of pictorial material, it seemed to me possible to use mere words instead of pictures. If words had any significant connotation, then, one might argue, it should be possible to get differential responses to words from different individuals. An added feature to this kind of research was that brightness differences posed no problem. We presented words in either white or black on a medium gray background. Both were used, and we found no essential differences in the results as a function of brightness.

We used words which were not particularly stimulating. Or at least so we thought. This was really a trial to see whether we could get any differentiation at all.

We found that with the longer words in white, thus essentially giving a larger amount of brightness stimulation, we were able to get pupil dilation. Two of the words which received the highest increase in pupil diameter when viewed by the subjects were the words "pleasure" and "hospitality." Opposed to this, a smaller word, which had less brightness caused constriction. It was "thirst." We did enough work along this general line to indicate the usefulness of this particular approach and did not do a longer study. Rather, I reported the results of these findings at meetings and discussed them with the stream of visitors we had in our laboratory. The technique was soon picked up and a number of papers involving the use of such material appeared in the ensuing years. Two workers at the University of Eastern Ontario, Allan Paivio and Herb Simpson, using a total of 34 adult subjects showed words to these subjects in the same manner as we have been doing in our laboratory. These words, all nouns, were shown to the subjects and were varied in two ways, concreteness versus abstractness and pleasantness versus unpleasantness. Candy, mucous, charm, sadness, are examples of the four kinds of words. The subjects were requested to imagine an object or an event related to each of the words which was shown. It was shown that the subjects had greater pupil dilation to abstract words than to concrete words. Not only was pupil dilation consistently greater to abstract words but pupil dilation in response to the task of mentally imagining the meaning of a concrete word diminished to the control level demonstrably sooner than pupil dilation in response to the task of mental imagery to an abstract word. The two workers considered these findings as physiological evidence that it is more difficult to generate images to abstract words like disease than to concrete words like honeycomb.

On the other hand, Paivio and Simpson did not find any differences in pupillary behavior to pleasant as compared to unpleasant words. This difference from the findings obtained in our own laboratories with respect to pictorial stimuli and even with some of the early studies using words may arise from the fact that different tasks were asked of the subjects and that the mental activity involved in the imagery task may have inhibited any constriction effects that might otherwise have occurred to words. This also was concluded by these two workers. Several other researchers, using word stimuli and pooled subject data, nevertheless have concluded the pupil response is not differentially affected by positive and negative affect states.

However, we found a completely different response in a 1968 word study which was carried on in our laboratory largely under the leadership of Dr. James Polt. We used four words: hostile, squirm, flay, and nude. These words were each prepared in two different sizes on slides as we had done previously for pictures and were shown to men and to women.

One reason we carried out the study was that while people seem to have characteristic responses to pictures, the reactions of *individuals* to words presented on the screen of the perception apparatus are extremely variable and not very predictable. That is, it is not possible to predict precisely the emotional effect a given word will have on a particular person in the same way that it is possible for us to predict positive responses from men to female pinup pictures or from women to pictures of babies.

Our study of the effects of single words was carried out not only with the idea of surveying differences in response to these words by individuals and by men and women, but also with the idea of looking into the effect of the size of the word on the pupil response. Although the mental arithmetic studies carried out by different researchers have shown that the characteristic pupillary behavior during mental calculations is not caused by changes in eye focusing, it has not been shown whether the proportion of the visual field that a word or picture takes up affects the pupillary response to them. The technical term for this factor is "visual angle"; that is, a circle at a small distance away takes up more of the visual field than it does at a farther distance, so that a larger circle is required for the same visual angle to be taken up, "subtended," at the farther distance.

When the words were projected on the screen of the perception apparatus, the small size was ¾ of an inch in height and the larger size was twice as tall, 1½ inches. Thus we had eight words alternated with numbered control slides shown to each subject for periods of ten seconds each. Half of the subjects saw the words in one order and the other half saw them in the reverse order. Just as with other studies the pupil sizes in the film records were measured to obtain the ten-second "control" sizes and the ten-second "word" sizes.

Nine men and six women were shown these words. They were

all students or assistants in the Psychology Department at the University of Chicago. Their ages ranged from 24 to 45 years.

The pupil responses of these subjects showed no significant difference to the words as a function of large or small size. The mean response to the large words was −.4 per cent, which is within random fluctuation from control level. The mean response to the small words was +.1 per cent, which is also within random fluctuation. The mean response of the pupil to the first large word presented ("squirm" for half of the subjects, "hostile" for the other half) was +1.2 per cent, and +.7 per cent for the first small word presented ("hostile" for half of the subjects, "flay" for the other half). The second large word ("flay" for half of the subjects, "nude" for the other half) resulted in a mean pupil response of −2.0 per cent from the subjects and the second small word ("nude" for half of the subjects, "squirm" for the other half) resulted in a mean pupil response of −.5 per cent. The comparison of the responses to the first and second words shows a downward trend which is also reflected in the comparison of the first and second presentations of the same word (see Table 1).

**Table 1   Mean Changes in Pupil Size to Four Words on Two Presentations**

Changes are in per cent plus or minus from the previous control period.

|  | Presentation 1 | | Presentation 2 | |
|---|---|---|---|---|
|  | Male | Female | Male | Female |
| hostile | −1.5 | +1.9 | −1.4 | −4.1 |
| squirm | −2 | −1.5 | +.1 | −1.5 |
| flay | +4.7 | −.2 | +.8 | −2 |
| nude | +3.8 | +1.8 | .0 | −3.4 |

From Polt, J. M. and Hess, E. H. *Psychonomic Science*, **12**, 389–390 (1960).

However, because of the large variability between the individual subjects the difference between the large and small words is not statistically significant. At any rate it does not appear likely that the pupil responses to the smaller words are to be accounted for by the subjects trying to "see" the smaller words.

The average, mean, responses of the men and the women to

the four words, regardless of size, during the two presentations are shown in Table 2. While distinct differences between the men and the women are evident, none of these differences is statistically significant, again because of individual variability. The word "flay" appeared to evoke a particularly strong emotional response in the men the first time they saw it, as evidenced by the positive average response to it. The same appeared to be true in the case of the word "nude," a word to which the women also had a strong dilation. The words "flay" and "nude" probably evoked the most imagery in the subjects. The only word which had an increased dilation during its second presentation in comparison with its first presentation was the word "squirm," and this was on the part of the men. In other cases the response either went down or remained the same.

**Table 2   Range of Dilation and Constriction of Individual Male and Female Ss When First Presented with Four Words**

Changes are in per cent plus or minus from
the previous control period.

| | Male | | Female | |
| --- | --- | --- | --- | --- |
| | High | Low | High | Low |
| hostile | + 8 | − 12.3 | + 6 | − 2.3 |
| squirm | + 12 | − 15.3 | + 7.7 | − 8 |
| flay | + 34.5 | − 11.2 | + 14.2 | − 6.3 |
| nude | + 26.1 | − 14.9 | + 14.6 | − 5.3 |

From Polt, J. M. and Hess, E. H. *Psychonomic Science*, **12** 389–390 (1960).

Table 2 shows the strongest positive and strongest negative responses elicited by each word (regardless of size or presentation) from men and from women subjects. These highly individual differences shown in this table are, of course, completely obscured when group differences to the four words are computed. With the men the largest dilation in response to a word occurred in response to the word "flay," 45.7 per cent; while the word "squirm" elicited the most constriction, − 15.3 per cent, from a single man. Of considerable interest is the fact that the individual scores for the women subjects did not reach the extremes that the individual scores for the men subjects did: the largest dilation from a woman subject occurred in response to the word "nude" (14.6 per cent), and the strongest constriction from a woman occurred in response to the word "squirm" ($-8$ per cent).

The considerably greater total range in individual responses for men than for women (more than twice as much) is in accord with some other results which we have obtained, for example, the responses to sounds which in themselves have no meanings. Dr. Benjamin Beck, one of my former students, found that the pupil responses of men were greater than they were for women in response to varying rates of a click noise. We have as yet no good explanation for this. It would be easy enough to come to the conclusion that there is greater mental activity on the part of men than on the part of women, but I am sure that such a view would scarcely meet with popular support—particularly from women who might retort that the greater pupil response from the men shows that they have to work harder to process sensory information! Or perhaps men have greater autonomic lability as described by H. J. Eysenck, since R. D. Francis found that normal neuroticism is associated with greater pupil responses to spoken words.

The results of this study show that a constriction response to words very clearly occurs. However, it must be noted that the constriction response is an extremely *individualistic* matter. It could amount to perceptual vigilance or perceptual protection occurring whenever the nature of the arousal associated with a specific word is threatening to the subject. In such cases, then, the constriction response could serve to "shut out" the word. Although the constrictive response certainly will remain a controversial topic, this study not only demonstrates that it exists, but also that it is not a phenomenon that is apparent in a pooled group of people. It is restricted to the individual level, and we cannot predict precisely what will be a "negative" stimulus to that individual.

## THE CONSTRICTION RESPONSE

We are getting more research data which continue to confirm this original finding and hypothesis on negative pupil responses and there are, fortunately, still more research studies by others which also confirm this finding. Such studies include one by Jerry Dean Barlow in 1969. In this investigation he used actual political participation as a criterion for selecting subjects and which obtained pupil constriction in response to a picture of the major opposition politician. White conservative supporters of George Wallace had pupil dilation to Wallace's picture and pupil constriction to a picture of Lyndon Johnson and to a picture of the late Martin Luther King, Jr. Both white and black liberals had pupil constriction to Wallace's picture and pupil dilation to pictures of Johnson and King. The black liberals, furthermore, had more extreme constriction and dilation responses to these pictures than did the white liberals, presumably because of their emotional involvement. Since Barlow and I worked independently I do not believe that we both fortuitously obtained this bidirectional pupil response result.

In addition, another study, by Robert W. Atwood and Robert J. Howell, has demonstrated differential pupil responses of constriction and dilation. This study involved ten female-aggressing pedophiliacs who were serving jail sentences for having nonviolently molested female children less than 12 years old. The ten control subjects were inmates of the same jail and were not sexual offenders. All subjects were shown pictures of attractive adult females and of immature females. The pedophiliacs' pupils dilated to the pictures of young females and constricted to the pictures of adult females; whereas the nondeviate males' pupils dilated to the pictures of adult females and either constricted or showed no change in half of the cases when the young female pictures were shown. The group means of the two subject groups were clearly very different. While individual differences among the subjects were also apparent in this study, the responses within each group were consistent, with one subject in each experimental group giving pupil responses that indicated further aspects of their sexual attitudes.

Furthermore, Richard S. Fredericks, using 25 pictorial stimuli on 45 male subjects obtained highly significant results in favor of my dilation-constriction hypothesis, since his analysis of variance and correlation data showed that dilation was associated with pleasant stimuli and constriction with unpleasant stimuli. A joint report by Fredericks and Marion H. Groves reaffirms these conclusions. Herbert L. Coverdale has reported that while pupillary constriction responses are relatively low in frequency, normal subjects having high neuroticism scores show a significantly higher frequency of pupillary constriction than any of the other personality groups he studied, which included introverts, extraverts, and stables.

In contrast to the studies demonstrating the existence of pupillary constriction responses is one by John J. Woodmansee in which it was concluded that pupil constriction does not occur to negative affect. Figure 2, page 525, of Woodmansee's report shows a graph of the pupil responses of equalitarian and anti-black female college students to pictures of blacks and to control slides.

**Table 3   Estimated Pupil Diameter Size Changes from Control to Racial Content Test Stimuli in 11 Equalitarian and 11 Anti-Black Female Subjects During the First Presentation of Stimuli***

| Subjects | First Stimulus | Second Stimulus | Third Stimulus | Fourth Stimulus |
|----------|---------------|-----------------|----------------|-----------------|
| Equalitarian | +3.5% | +2.6% | +1.7% | +2.5% |
| Anti-Black | +1.9% | + .5% | − .3% | −2.0% |

* Data based upon measurement of points on Figure 2, page 525 of: Woodmansee, J. J. The pupil response as a measure of social attitudes. In: G. F. Summers (Ed.), *Attitude Measurement.* Chicago, Illinois: Rand McNally, 1970. The percentage changes for each stimulus were computed by taking the difference in pupil size during the viewing of the test stimulus and during the viewing of the control which preceded it, and then calculating the percentage by which the pupil changed its size from that of the control period when the test stimulus was viewed.

While it is obvious from Table 3 that the equalitarian subjects' pupils consistently dilated to the stimulus pictures, Woodmansee's interpretation of the pupil behavior of the anti-black subjects is quite different from mine. In my view, these subjects' pupils dilated to the first picture primarily because of the well-known "first picture effect." A slight dilation occurs to the second picture, and a rather slight constriction to the third picture. There is very definitely a pupil constriction to the fourth stimulus.

Woodmansee has proposed that in order to assess pupil

dilation and pupil constriction properly, pupil diameters during the control periods both before and after a given stimulus should be averaged together. While the control period pupil diameters declined slightly and gradually for the equalitarian subjects, either because of slight boredom or relaxation, the anti-black subjects showed a rather rapidly decreasing control pupil size. Woodmansee attributes this to arousal decrement, but I would attribute it to emotional carry-over from the stimuli to the control periods. I would attribute it to an increasing avoidance of the negatively toned experimental situation on the part of these subjects. Certainly their pupil behavior during control and stimulus slides after the second stimulus picture is dramatically different from that of the equalitarian subjects. There is no way that I am able to escape this conclusion.

I should point out, however, that my interpretation follows the same line of thinking that may be found in research by Jum C. Nunnally, Paul D. Knott, Albert Duchnowski and Ronald Parker with respect to the effect of lifting different weights upon pupil size. In this study, pupil sizes between the lifting of weights did not return to the same control level. The magnitude of the pupil size during the control period between weight liftings corresponded to the subject's *anticipation* of the weight to be lifted next. The subjects clearly were not always in an affectively neutral or relaxed state between the weight liftings.

I feel that I should further point out that it is not true that "control" pupil sizes are always at the neutral level corresponding strictly to the amount of illumination. Indeed, a control interval not only functions to account for total brightness effects but also aids to partially account for emotional carry-over from the previous stimulus situation. Since emotional carry-overs dissipate, there is always less emotional carry-over during the stimulus than during the previous control period. Nevertheless the use of the immediately preceding control period pupil size permits a more accurate assessment of the effect of the particular stimulus being shown than does the use of illumination level effects only. Sequential effects such as a subject's getting bored are also important to control for. This can be done at least in part through the control period just before each stimulus, so that the relative effect of the stimulus may be assessed. Or, if the subject should happen to start thinking of extraneous things, such as events that will occur at the end of the experiment, then these can also be at least partially controlled for by the use of the previous control period. This methodology is similar to that used by ethologists in studying the relative effectiveness of different stimuli in releasing specific behaviors in animals.

After the initial attacks upon the psychosensory pupil constriction concept, I began to have some serious doubts as to the validity of such a hypothesis because a two-directional indicator of this sort did not seem to make too much sense, at least not on the surface. It is perfectly clear that if there is no mental activity whatsoever and the subject is unconscious, asleep, or dead, there is extreme constriction, that is, the pupil is only a couple of millimeters in diameter. Any mental activity will then cause the pupil to get larger. All this of course assumes the absence of light, and the pupil, with varying degrees of arousal, will get larger and larger until it reaches the maximum of eight or nine millimeters which is about a fourfold increase in pupil diameter. What now appears to me extremely sensible is to look at the pupil changes in both a positive and negative sense, that is, both in dilation and constriction in the following way. Suppose a certain level of arousal (under, of course, constant conditions of light) is causing the pupil to be, say, four millimeters in size. The presentation of positive material can now cause dilation or the presentation of negative material can cause some constriction. This makes it a two-dimensional system, in spite of the fact that the basic pupil change is of course, merely one of dilation if one considers its starting point to be *complete constriction.* In this regard, it is no different from our concept of hot and cold which is merely a deviation from our normal average body temperature because temperature as a measure obviously is also a one-directional indicator if taken in an absolute sense. There is no such thing as cold: there is merely more or less heat, starting from absolute zero. In the same way, one could say there is no such thing as constriction, that there is only dilation as taken from the absolute zero of total mental activity. However, just as it is possible for us to have a frame of reference for our own body temperature and talk about a two-directional system of warm, hot, cool, and cold, we can also deal with a positive and negative response involving a variation from the average or normal or "body temperature" type of pupil size.

We will discuss later other ways in which one can get to the root of this problem and deal with a more substantial evaluation of negative material, including the kind of material which is sufficiently arousing, startling, or shocking that any negative response, that is, a constriction response, is completely obscured by the shocking nature of the material. This results in a mild kind of fright reaction that is well known in scientific and popular literature to cause pupil dilation because of the autonomic system activation that occurs under such conditions. For example, a picture of a can of worms often causes women's pupils to constrict, but a real can of worms probably would cause the pupils of these women to dilate. Not only that, but the type of picture that causes constriction often appears to be a rather individual matter. What causes constriction in one person may cause dilation in another. It is very difficult to make a *priori* judgments as to what pictures will be unpleasant for a given individual. Certainly that individual's verbally expressed attitudes may not truly reflect actual feelings.

Let us now look at some of the pictures which we have found to have good positive responses. As indicated in our first study, certain kinds of pinups produced predictably good responses on the part of male subjects and this has held up in studies involving hundreds of subjects. One such picture is a super-optimally bosom shaped, nude female pinup which appeared in a popular men's magazine. The fact that the response may not be much different in another part of the world has been shown by a study which was carried out simultaneously in New York, London, and Paris. While there were different reactions to some other pictorial material, the men had the largest response to the picture of this pinup and the women on the whole had negative responses. There are some pictures that have usually resulted in negative responses on the part of some subjects. A concentration camp picture gave the strongest individual constriction that we have had in the laboratory, approximately 20 per cent. We also found a strong constriction when we showed certain types of modern art.

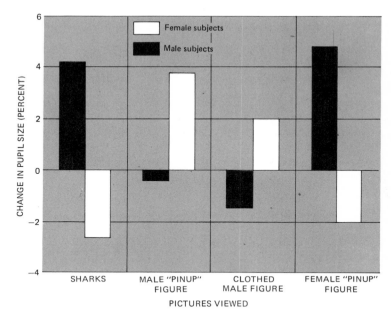

**Figure 8**   The pupil responses of men and women to four different pictures. Each picture was preceded by an unlighted screen, rather than by a control slide matched for average brightness, as is usually done. Therefore, the stimulus slide caused more light to fall upon the eyes than there had been during the previous control period. If illumination level were the sole factor influencing pupil size, the pupils of the subjects should have constricted to every stimulus slide. Yet, as this graph shows, some subjects showed pupil dilation responses to some of the slides. The black bars show the increase or decrease in the pupil diameter of the men subjects during the viewing of each stimulus slide in comparison with the previous control period. The white bars give the same data for the women subjects. (From Hess, E. H., Attitude and pupil size. *Scientific American*, **212**, No. 4, 46–54 (1965). Copyright © 1965 by Scientific American, Inc. All rights reserved.)

This, in particular, is one of those instances in which there are large individual response differences. We will have more to say about that shortly.

In one of the experiments conducted a short time after we had done our initial work and where we were particularly interested in constriction, we tried, with only four pictures, to see what differences we could get between men and women looking at: (1) sharks, (2) a male pinup figure, (3) a clothed male, and (4) a female pinup picture. We did something further. That was to use no control slide before each of the photographs shown but instead to have the screen dark for the ten seconds preceding the showing of the slide. The results showed extremely clear sex differences, as shown in Figure 8. Of particular interest is the fact that the clothed male figure was one which we obtained from a magazine published in Greenwich Village for homosexuals and one could notice that the female response to that particular picture was much less than that for a "normal" male nude. This slide actually was one which we used in a study of homosexuals which we will soon discuss. In the present experiment we also had a large average negative response on the part of our male subjects—a response which is statistically significant. The only part of our results which is not understandable is the very high positive response obtained from the males for the picture of the sharks. One clue for this peculiar outcome may be what one of our subjects said after the experiment. It was clear when he talked about the pictures that he thought them to be porpoises or dolphins rather than sharks. Since the picture was not terribly clear, it offered some interesting suggestions that we might, with somewhat ambiguous pictures perceivable as positive or negative, be able to get a good idea as to how the subject views or perceives any picture without asking for that information or without the possibility of the subject being able to lie about which way he saw the picture. This particular experiment, as well as others, have shown very definite sex differences in the results. They are also to be found in a number of studies which have since been published by other investigators.

## THE TACHISTOSCOPIC EXPOSURE AND SUBLIMINAL PERCEPTION

Psychologists, along with many other scientists, frequently use big words to describe rather simple things. One about which many jokes are made by psychology students and researchers alike is the *tachistoscopic episcotister.* It is a fairly complex name, extremely difficult to pronounce, to describe a very simple device. What it does is to allow the flashing of some visual material on a screen or into the eye of the subject for a part of a second. For example, we might want to show a picture on a screen in front of a subject and not give him very much time to look at it—let us say perhaps only a tenth of a second or a fiftieth of a second. Using this sort of device psychologists have long tested the ability of people to recognize certain types of visual material. For example, they find that in the case of those things which the subject does not particularly care to see, a much longer exposure time is required in order for it to be seen. In other words, the subject may have to be shown a picture at a fitieth of a second, then a fortieth, a thirtieth, and a tenth and a fifth before he finally admits that he has seen it. The use of this device has also been prevalent in advertising research, particularly in the recognition of certain package designs where clear and quick visibility and recognition are important. It should be apparent to the reader that the pupil technique might lend itself extremely well for use when we want to find out whether the subject is really telling the truth insofar as his failure or admitted failure, to see the stimulus is concerned. The general scheme is a simple one. We know, for example, that except in special medical or neurological cases, a simple flash of light always produces a pupil constriction. If we flash a light in the eyes of a normal subject (and this sort of work has been done for years), we get the following changes in the pupil. At a point before any light has been flashed, we can measure the response of the subject for that particular level of illumination. Immediately upon receiving the flash of light, in a fraction of a second, the pupil constricts, and we can see this in the diagram. However, the recovery from the flash of light is quick and the pupil diameter increases and sometimes becomes a little larger than it was originally. If the pupil becomes larger than it was just before perceiving the flash of light, it then quickly returns to a baseline which is about the same as it was before the flash of light was shown. Figure 9 shows the pupil response of a single subject to a .2 second flash of light. The points on this figure show the mean pupil size of the subject for each of the 16 frames taken per second. The circled points represent every fourth frame, and thus show that 4 frames each second provide good reliability for depicting the course of the pupil reflex. Hence we subsequently used frames taken every .25 second for our data. The ordinate on the graph gives the pupil size as magnified 16.5 times. That is, before the onset of the light flash the pupils averaged slightly less than 5 millimeters in diameter and then constricted to slightly less than 4 millimeters in diameter. The constriction response reached its maximum in .5 second. Recovery to the previous illumination level was almost complete 2 seconds after the flash.

Quite by accident the influence of auditory stimulation upon the photopupil reflex was studied. This happened because the film used for recording pupillary behavior moves through a clicking film transport mechanism within the Bolex movie camera. Consequently, the faster the filming rate, the more clicks per second and the greater the auditory stimulation given to the subjects. We had used two different filming speeds, eight frames per second and four frames per second. Subsequently, we also tested some subjects with the camera so muffled that the subjects

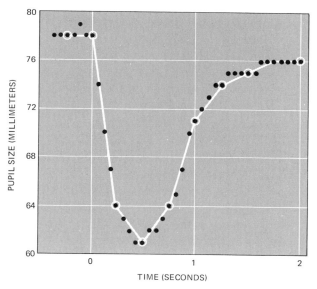

TIME (SECONDS)

**Figure 9** Pupil size of a normal human subject in response to a .2 second light flash which began at 0 seconds. Sixteen frames per second were taken of the pupil. As may be seen, the pupil reached its minimum size in less than half a second after the light flash began. The circled points represent every fourth frame, and thus show that four frames per second are sufficient to record the photopupil reflex. (From "Die normale und die gestörte Pupillenbewegung. Symposion der Deutschen Ophthalmologischen Gesellschaft 1972" (1973) © J. F. Bergmann Verlag München.)

did not report hearing clicks. Thus there were three different subject groups with five subjects in each group: those who heard eight clicks per second, those who heard four clicks per second, and those who apparently heard nothing.

Figure 10 depicts the stylized pupil responses to .2 second light flashes under the different auditory conditions. These pupil responses are stylized in the sense that straight lines are drawn · from the beginning of the constriction phase to the smallest pupil size, and from the smallest pupil size to the beginning of the "E" wave (described by Otto Löwenstein and Irene E.

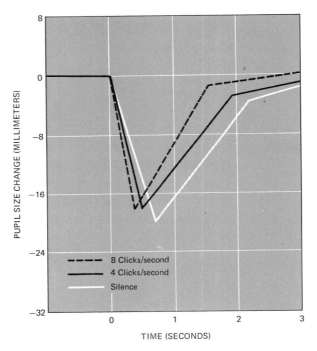

**Figure 10**   Pupil responses of normal human subjects to a .2 second light flash under three different auditory conditions: silence, four clicks per second, and eight clicks per second. The pupil response curve is a stylized representation of the sequential pupil sizes during and after the flashed light. The curve is stylized in the sense that a straight line is drawn from the original control size to the smallest size, and two straight lines are drawn to represent the two major phases of redilatation after the minimum size has been reached. (From "Die normale und die gestörte Pupillenbewegung. Symposion der Deutschen Ophthalmologischen Gesellschaft 1972" (1973) © J. F. Bergmann Verlag München.)

Loewenfeld in 1950), and from the beginning of the "E" wave to the point where the pupil size begins to stabilize. Thus this graph shows in schematic form the two major stages of redilatation after the constriction response: the "D" and the "E" waves described by Löwenstein and Loewenfeld. As can be seen from this figure, the effect of the auditory stimulation is that it prevents the pupil from constricting as fully as it does under conditions of silence and promotes a more rapid redilation—with eight clicks per second having stronger effects upon the photopupil reflex than four clicks per second. Benjamin B. Beck has done research extensively exploring the effects of auditory stimulation upon the photopupil reflex and his research raises questions about the use of some of the noisier pupillometric devices.

With this baseline information we used a camera filming rate of four frames per second for the next series of flashes. Five human males and five human females were used as subjects. They were presented with a control light flash, a slide of a female nude, and a slide of concentration camp victims; all of which lasted .2 second, with 10 seconds between each flashed presentation.

Figure 11 shows the stylized pupil responses of the male subjects. The pupil response to the control flash is almost identical with that for the four clicks per second auditory conditions in Figure 10. While the flashed picture of the female nude did not substantially change the photopupil reflex except for producing a pupil size larger than the one for the plain light flash during the third second after presentation, the flashed picture of concentration camp victims had a marked effect. The subjects' pupils constricted at the same rate as for the control or female nude flash, but kept on constricting rather than redilating so that a much smaller pupil size was reached before the redilatation phases began. Furthermore, at the end of the third second the pupils were still well below the original control size and were beginning to stablize at that level. The response to the female nude, with the pupil larger than for the control by the third second is of course in agreement with male responses in the usual manner in which slides are shown for 10 seconds.

Figure 12 depicts the pupil responses of the five female

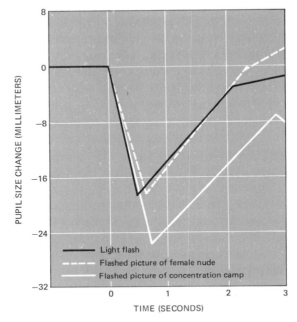

**Figure 11**   Stylized pupil response curve depicting the photopupil reflexes of normal male humans to a .2 second flashed light and to two different .2 second flashed pictures. The black line depicts the stylized response to the light flash; the dashed line depicts the stylized response to the flashed picture of a female nude; and the solid white line depicts the stylized response to the flashed picture of a concentration camp. (From "Die normale und die gestörte Pupillenbewegung. Symposion der Deutschen Ophthalmologischen Gesellschaft 1972" (1973) © J. F. Bergmann Verlag München.)

subjects to the same series of three flashes. Their photopupil reflex to the control flash was essentially identical to that of the males as was their photopupil reflex to the flashed picture of the concentration camp victims. That is, constriction was noticeably greater than that for the simple light flash and the "D" wave began at a smaller pupil size than it had for the simple light flash. But the females' photopupil reflex to the flashed picture of a female nude was very different from that of the males. In their case pupil constriction proceeded as long as it had for the concentration camp picture, but did not reach as small a size. Redilation thus occurred sooner for the female nude picture than for the concentration camp picture, and the "E" wave began at a definitely later time than it had for the control flash. Furthermore, at the end of the third second, the pupils were at the same level as they had been for the concentration camp picture.

The amount of pupil constriction from flashed pictures, as can easily be measured by the drop in pupil size that is seen in each of the figures, may vary. It may be a lot greater for a negative stimulus than it is for a positive stimulus. This, too, gives us an additional measure of the value of a particular picture for a particular subject.

Here, especially, it is extremely important that we not use the pooled or averaged results of a large number of people for many

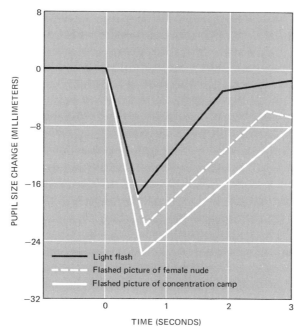

**Figure 12** Stylized pupil response curve depicting the photopupil reflexes of normal female subjects to a .2 second flashed light and to two different .2 second flashed pictures. The black line depicts the stylized response to the light flash; the dashed line depicts the stylized response to the flashed picture of a female nude; and the solid white line depicts the stylized response to the flashed picture of a concentration camp. (From "Die normale und die gestörte Pupillenbewegung. Symposion der Deutschen Ophthalmologischen Gesellschaft 1972" (1973) © J. F. Bergmann Verlag München.)

of our experimental procedures if we want to get some insight into what is going on. For example, we may work with a number of subjects, some of whom like a certain stimulus and some of whom dislike it. Let us say that we have ten subjects who like to look at a certain kind of picture; in other words, it is pleasing to them and they all get a 10 per cent increase in pupil diameter. This certainly is not to be found in such a precise manner, but I am using it simply for the purpose of illustration. Let us say that the other ten people have a constriction, that is, the same stimulus is unpleasant to them and they all show a 10 per cent decrease in pupil size. If we combine the results of our twenty subjects, something that is commonly done in laboratory experimental procedures and certainly also in the advertising research world, we will end up with a response that will indicate no change. In other words, there will be a zero change from the previous control level. Obviously this procedure obscures the fundamental process and eliminates from our knowledge a tremendous amount of information. The reasons why ten people find one thing stimulating and positive and ten others find the same stimulus to be negative are of the utmost importance in determining the meaning and value of the material that is to be tested.

Now let us return to our tachistoscopic material. In using this procedure of flashed presentation it has been easy for us to determine whether a subject who stated that he was not able to see the stimulus or gave us an erroneous and perhaps mild version of what he saw was actually telling the truth. If he is really unable to see the stimulus there ought to be no change of the sort which I have discussed. In fact, his response ought to be as it is for a plain light flash. Pupil responses for a rather uninteresting landscape are very similar to those for a mere flash of light. We have found in some instances that pictures which ought to be meaningful for a certain individual were reported as not seen, but the pupil evidence was quite to the contrary. This is particularly true for value-loaded material which society may frown upon and which the experimental subject might not be too happy to discuss.

This can occur entirely on the unconscious level. Many times social pressures produce effects which are quite automatic and unnoticeable to the individual. It may be, for example, so highly anxiety-provoking to have an attitude that runs counter to the perceived official social norms, with the result that such an attitude tends to be repressed from the individual's consciousness. Much of our data, in fact, have lent a great deal of support to the notion of "perceptual defense" that has been so hotly debated in psychology. Perceptual defense refers to the notion that the individual avoids perceiving things which are anxiety-provoking, particularly when they involve socially tabooed things.

When socially disapproved, anxiety-arousing, or taboo words are tachistoscopically flashed on a screen, subjects usually find them much harder to recognize than neutral words. The psychopupil constriction response has been suggested as a possible mechanism by which this occurs. Indeed Lemly D. Hutt and J. Anderson have conducted research on this question. Hutt determined the tachistoscopic recognition thresholds for words of three different categories of emotional response—pleasant, unpleasant, and taboo. He also recorded the pupil response to these words when projected on a screen. Pupil size and recognition threshold values were found to be significantly and negatively correlated. The correlation coefficients were significant in the taboo and pleasant categories whereas they did not reach significance within the unpleasant category. This experiment did not, of course, show that the pupil sizes were causally related to recognition thresholds.

Our experiments not only support the notion of perceptual defense, but also give some information as to some of the factors occurring during this phenomenon. The negative pupil size changes occur in response to anxiety-provoking material seen by the subject. Hence, the *verbalized* recognition threshold must also be a function of anxiety-provoking characteristics of the material viewed rather than of the pupil size, because as we have shown, the pupil size in response to tachistoscopically presented material is a function of *actual* recognition.

I cannot overstress that pupil constriction phenomena normally cannot be obtained by pooling subject data, particularly in the case of negatively toned pictorial stimuli. The positive-negative aspect of the emotional responses elicited by tachistoscopic pictures is an extremely individualistic matter. Furthermore, I feel constrained to point out that the classical photopupil reflex curve normally cannot be obtained in a single trial with a single human subject. As we all know, the curves published in the literature are based on pooled data. The classical photopupil reflex is an abstraction that does not normally occur in a real situation. It is only a tendency of the pupil to react in this way to flashed light. Other factors intervene to cause the pupils of individual subjects to deviate from the classical curve during the individual trials. I would like to suggest that an important reason why this is so is that when a human subject is placed in an experiment of this kind various notions and ideas can occur to him. When they do, they exert dilating or constricting influences upon the pupil and therefore the resulting photopupil reflex curve for a given subject deviates accordingly. What the tachistoscopic picture presentation does, in effect, is to control to some degree just what it is that crosses the subject's mind during and immediately after the light flash.

I think it is quite apparent that there are advantages to the use of tachistoscopic presentation, although it lends itself only to a restricted amount of material since the subject has little time to "look" at something and certainly no chance to scan it or to look at different parts of the picture. In the actual procedure the technique used is very simple. The subject is placed in front of the apparatus and the rear projection screen is illuminated to a moderate level. A small black spot is used so that he can fix his eyes on it. We start taking pupil pictures when his eye is of a reasonable size, that is, when he has become adapted to that amount of light which will make the pupil half open, about 4 to 5 millimeters in diameter. Then every so many seconds, we merely flash one of the pictures of our series. This means that we do not have a control if we do not want it. In other words, we do not need to present a control slide, but if we do (and often we do just that) it gives us additional information about the presentation of a neutral, completely meaningless, light flash. In this way, we expect to find a difference between the kind of response we get when we flash a neutral control slide and the kind of response we get when we flash a meaningful photograph of one sort or another. Indeed, these are the results that we have obtained. There is extreme similarity, almost identity, between the results that we find for the different control slides. The pupil response for them can be superimposed one over the other, and they all look like the one for the simple light flash. But the responses for the meaningful pictures varying from pleasant or exciting scenes to horror or unpleasant ones, give quite different patterns of change, as has been shown in some of the illustrations. And with this, either after showing the flashed picture or later, perhaps after we have shown the subject five different kinds of pictures, we can ask what he remembers seeing. It has been found, in general, that the picture that was not reported as having been seen would often be the one that caused the most constriction or dilation, in comparison with that which would ordinarily result from a simple light flash.

The fact that positive and negative affective responses to the flashed pictures can be demonstrated proves that the subjects actually saw the flashed pictures. This conclusion is inescapable if their pupil sizes deviate from those shown for flashes of simple light. The presence of unrecognizable visual patterning within the light flash when pictures are presented cannot be solely responsible since the experiments have also shown that landscapes and the control slide used in my pupillometric research both produce the very same photopupil reflex that simple light flashes do. Also, these findings are congruent with Gad Hakerem's and Samuel Sutton's report that pupil dilations accompany the recognition or detection of visual stimuli that are near to the visual threshold.

Subliminal perception is a variation of the tachistoscopic exposure method. It once aroused public concern to the extent that even Congress became concerned about it. It is illustrated by a sponsor repeatedly superimposing on the screen a quickly flashed picture, scarcely perceptible, or perhaps, as many people argued, not perceptible on a conscious level, during the showing of a motion picture in a theatre or on the television screen at home. This quickly flashed picture would be of some sort of package or product shown in the hope of creating a certain attitude or desire in the subjects.

Let us take a crass example. Suppose you are sitting in a motion picture theatre and you are watching a rerun of *Gone With the*

*Wind,* and every so often very quickly—for just a fraction of a second—during the carryings on of Clark Gable and Vivian Leigh, there appears on the screen very faintly but still somehow registering on your mind, a picture of a popcorn box. The idea of some of the people who developed this whole procedure and tried to profit from it commercially was that it would indeed cause many more people to get up and buy a box of popcorn at the candy counter.

This was considered to be such a terrible sort of brainwashing over which the public had no control that the whole procedure was banned. Actually it was a ridiculous situation from the beginning. For example, it is to me no different whatever from showing a television commercial which is designed to do the same thing. It is just that we are not particularly interrupted with our general train of thought as we watch the program being shown. In fact it might be best if all television commercials were reduced periodically to this kind of tachistoscopic presentation in which the sponsor would show his product but would not particularly interfere with the showing of the midnight movie. The second reason why it is ridiculous is that there is no good experimental evidence which indicates that it indeed caused any greater amount of behavioral response on the part of the subjects who were exposed to this type of material than if they were shown something outright. It is but another technique in the long sequence of attempts to try to convince or to change the attitude of the American public toward a consumer product.

One last point should obviously be made and that is that our own research has shown conclusively that you either give the response or you do not give it. That is, you either see the picture or you don't see it. Of course, the subject may not always know that he has seen the picture, particularly if social pressures are involved. For example, a woman may not know that she likes to look at pictures of nude men, because of the strong cultural pressures for women not to express such attitudes. If the flash exposure is so quick that the subject cannot tell what he is seeing, then we get no pupil change to indicate that he has actually seen the object shown. When the picture becomes recognizable, that is, when the subject is able to report that he has seen it, then we get the kind of change that is indicated as different from that obtained when we use a control slide.

Subliminal exposure or subliminal stimulus means merely that a certain input, in this case something presented visually, is below the limen. "Limen" is a fancy word for "threshold." Obviously, if a stimulus is below the threshold of perceiving and of sensing it would seem to be very difficult to have this particular stimulus invade the mind. In some respects it reminds me a great deal of extrasensory perception. It is difficult to assume perception without some sort of a sensation. As a matter of fact, in any of the psychophysical work that is done one cannot separate perception and sensation, that is, one cannot have perception without sensation. A stimulus has to be perceived; hence extrasensory perception means that it is perception that goes beyond or without the necessity of a sensory input from whatever source. It is no surprise that both subliminal perception and extrasensory perception have long been abandoned orphans of the scientific world, although the subject comes up again and again and many people would like to believe in extrasensory perception. The facts themselves are clear: these two processes cannot be easily demonstrated in any scientific laboratory situation. However, we are constantly finding new ways in which information is transmitted from one organism to another and to close one's mind against the possibility of farfetched examples is unforgivable.

# 5

# More Things We Have Found

In the course of our work, we came across two principal classes of response to pictorial stimuli. One class I have called *universal responses*. By that I mean that they tend by and large to produce certain results in almost all our subjects. For example, pictures of babies, of mothers and babies, and of "cute" baby animals usually elicit pupil dilations, particularly on the part of women. It is interesting to note that Konrad Lorenz, the foremost ethologist of our time, has proposed the idea that babyishness or the appreciation of that quality is an instinctive response for man. In one of the earlier texts written on the subject of instinctive behavior and ethology a diagram as shown in Figure 13 was used to indicate how changes in facial proportions can cause the difference in the degree of babyishness which an individual or animal can have.

Anders L. Lange at the University of Stockholm became interested in our pupil research and used our technique to test whether or not these variations in proportion would actually cause changes in pupil size as one went from the adult to the more babyish stimulus. He found that indeed the pictures which had the greatest babyish quality elicited the largest pupil responses. We have found this to be true in some work in our own laboratory and will have more to say on the subject later on.

We have also found in our research that pictures of a cross-eyed child or of some other mild bodily deformity almost universally elicit negative responses from subjects.

We also have the principal class which we have called *idiosyncratic or individualistic responses*. These are responses to

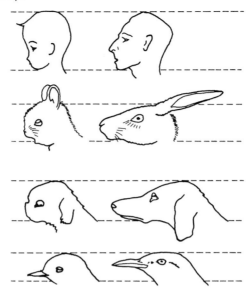

**Figure 13**   Young and adult heads of four different animal species. Comparison of the physical features shows the ways in which the features of the young differ from those of the adults. According to Konrad Lorenz, these infantile characteristics serve to release innately based parental caretaking reactions in adults. (From Lorenz, K. Z., Die angeborenen Formen möglicher Erfahrung. *Zeitschrift für Tierpsychologie*, **5,** 235–409, 1943.)

the same picture which can be, for one individual, extreme dilation or, for the next individual, a good constriction. Pictures eliciting such responses include examples of modern art and classic art, pictures of interior decorating types, pictures of automobiles, pictures of violence, pictures of individuals of two races interacting, pictures of patterns, objects, and even of mere designs. Indeed, this is not surprising because the variation of what visual things mean to people must be almost infinite. One such study is perhaps a good example of this. I mentioned previously that we used a picture of a male in a study of homosexuals.

In our earlier studies we found that some male subjects had a larger pupil response to pictures of their own sex than they did to pictures of the opposite sex. If the difference in pupil response toward pictures of male and female pinups on the part of men and women is truly a reflection of interest in the opposite sex as a sexual object, then it would appear that homosexuals should have stronger pupil responses to pictures of their own sex. We reviewed these anomalous cases which suggested that this might indeed be the situation. Thus we began a study of the pupil responses of both homosexual and heterosexual men to pictures of males and females. Allan L. Seltzer and John M. Shlien worked with me on this project.

Ten young adult men were tested. Five of them were students or workers in our laboratory whom we had known for some time and who served as the heterosexual group. Their sexual outlet was judged to be exclusively heterosexual. The other five men were known through observation, interview, and in every case by their own voluntary admission to one of the researchers who had gained their trust, to have overt homosexuality as their sole or primary sexual outlet. All ten of the subjects were about the same age, between 24 and 34 years, of the same educational status, with all but one being graduate students, and of the same social level. None of them was hospitalized or in therapy. None of the subjects was informed as to the nature of the stimuli that would be shown prior to their experimental exposure to them.

Fifteen pictures were shown. All of them were of the human figure, with the first picture and the last two being rather abstract cubist representations and therefore sexually unspecific. The second picture was of the crucifixion of Haman. These four pictures, and a fifth one (showing both a nude male and a nude female) placed in the middle of the series were classified as "art" pictures. They were included in the group of picture slides so as to place the obviously sexual pictures in an artistic setting and in this way reduce the potential threat that might be inherent in such material to some of the subjects. Many of the "female" pictures, in fact, were reproductions of famous paintings, while the "male" pictures were culled from homosexual magazines. Still another reason that the "art" pictures were added to the series was that of protecting against the "first stimulus" or novelty effect that is so often observable in our experiments. Also, homosexuals are often thought to have artistic interests, often taking up professions such as theatre arts, hairstyling, or interior decorating. Most of the homosexuals in this study did verbally indicate having such artistic inclinations.

The algebraic sum of the five percentage responses of the subjects to the five male pictures was used as the score for response to male pictures. The five percentage responses for the female pictures were similarly added together to obtain the score for response to the female pictures. The male and female response scores of each subject were subtracted algebraically to obtain a "relative male-female response" score, and these results are shown in Figure 14. In this way we had an indication of whether each subject's total response was greater toward males or females. If the score was positive this indicated that he had a greater total response to pictures of females than to males. If, on the other hand, the score was negative, this indicated that he had a greater total response to pictures of males than to females. The scores of the homosexual and heterosexual subjects, surprisingly enough, show no overlap. While one homosexual and one heterosexual subject show a very low total positive response, even in this case the score of the homosexual subject was lower than that of the heterosexual subject. Thus it is clear that the male-female response difference score discriminates between the two subject groups.

Some of the female pictures drew a high positive response from some of the homosexuals and some of the male pictures drew a high positive response from the heterosexuals. That is, response to any *single* picture did not serve to classify individuals as homosexual or heterosexual. However, the total response of a group of subjects to any single picture did serve to indicate whether that picture had homosexual or heterosexual appeal. The total heterosexual response to three of the five female pictures was positive, while the total homosexual response to each of the five male pictures was positive.

As for the artistic aspects of the pictures shown, the homosexuals, as a group, had a high pupil response to the artistically good but sexually vague picture slides, a high response to the artistically crude male pictures, and a low response to the artistically good female pictures. Thus it appears that pupillometrics can be useful as a means of experimentally studying artistic sensitivity.

Since we have improved our techniques of controlling brightness matching in pictures and controlling light-dark contrast, it may be possible to make up a test battery of pictorial stimuli that

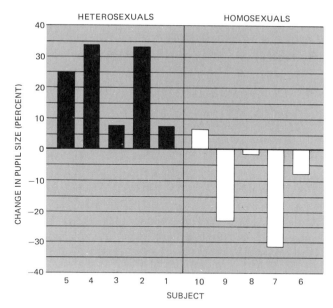

**Figure 14**   Depicted are the relative differences in pupil responses toward male and female pictures shown by individual heterosexual and homosexual subjects. A positive difference indicates a greater pupil response to pictures of females, whereas a negative difference indicates a greater pupil response to pictures of males. (From Hess, Eckhard H., Seltzer, Allan L., and Shlien, John M. Pupil response of hetero- and homosexual males to pictures of men and women: A pilot study. *Journal of Abnormal Psychology*, **70**, 165–168 (1965). Copyright 1965 by the American Psychological Association. Reprinted by permission.)

will permit an accurate determination of a single subject's sex preference. Of course, since *all* subjects saw exactly the same pictures the brightness factor could not in any way account for the differences between the individuals and between the two groups.

It should be noted that the cooperation of the homosexuals in participating in this study was unusual in that homosexuals normally have strong defenses against their identification as such. They all lived effectively in a normal environment, in school, at work, and with friends. Their sexual preferences were not at all obvious to the people who knew them, and they were ordinarily most reluctant to talk about or reveal their sexual interests. In spite of all this, their pupil responses differentiated them from heterosexual subjects. We cannot overemphasize, however, that this nonverbal response cannot serve as a predictor of actual homosexual behavior. All that has been shown is that where both sexual preferences and sexual behavior are homosexual, even if socially concealed, the pupil response can serve to discriminate such subjects from those having heterosexual preferences and behavior.

Another preliminary study conducted by us shows another way in which homosexual and normal men may be differentiated. We had a homosexual male "pinup" which was shown to a homosexual male and a normal male. We plotted the second-by-second size of the pupil diameter in relation to the control size during the ten-second period of viewing (see Figure 15). During this time the homosexual subject's pupil response started at a high positive level which gradually dropped during the ten seconds but which remained positive. With the normal subject, however, the pupil response was at first at the "non-interest" level, but as viewing continued there was a sharp drop in pupil size which then leveled off and remained at a distinctly negative level. It was as if the subject was at first noncommittal, and then adopted perceptual defenses against an obviously homosexual picture. In the light of such findings, I believe that further such study through the pupil response promises to produce fruitful findings and concepts.

Another study which we began almost ten years ago involves the pupil responses on the part of different people to photographs having some civil rights connotation. We had a number of photographs, one of them of a black man embracing a white woman and another one of a street scene with several blacks walking on the sidewalk, one of them carrying a gun, and other such photographs. Our subjects were drawn from the University community and all of them professed sympathy with the civil rights movement. The responses, however, were not consistent with their professed views. There were indeed some individuals, those whom one might, on the basis of one's own experience with them in their daily lives, consider to be liberal and supportive of the civil rights movement, who had good and positive responses. However, this was not true of one photo-

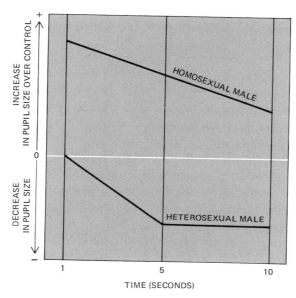

**Figure 15** Sequential pupil sizes during the viewing of a homosexually appealing picture of a man, as observed in a homosexually oriented man and in a heterosexually oriented man. Initially, the homosexual subject showed a pupil dilation to the picture while the heterosexual subject had no pupil change. Over the ten-second viewing period the homosexual subject showed a steady decline in interest which nevertheless remained positive. The heterosexual subject, however, soon showed a definite decrease in pupil size, and his pupil remained constricted to that smaller size for the remainder of the viewing period.

graph, the one in which there were several blacks, one of whom was carrying a gun. There, even the "liberal" had a negative response. In the case of some of our other individuals, even though the professed attitude was one of liberalism, there was a clear indication of a negative response, particularly to a picture involving sexual interaction between blacks and whites. If, again, one drew on knowledge about these individuals based on day to day contact, it was clear that these were either conservative individuals or ones who had been reared in the South.

This now really brings up a question and it is a most important one—what makes us think that the information we get from the individual's pupil response is any more real than the response we get by simply asking him, "Do you like it?" or "How much do you like it?" or "How much do you dislike it?" We have done a number of studies in an attempt to answer that question, and we have come to the unmistakable conclusion that regardless of what people *say,* we can get as true or truer indication of their attitude toward what is being shown them by means of pupillo-metrics as by questioning them. Let us look at some examples of what we have tried.

We made the assumption that probably people would be perfectly willing and able to tell us what they liked and what they disliked if we were dealing with material about which there was no strong social pressure to compel them to lie about or at least rationalize their answers. In the first experiment we showed pictures of five different types of food. After they had seen the pictures in the apparatus and had their pupil responses recorded, we showed them the pictures on a table and said, "Would you please arrange them in the order of the one you like the best to the one you like the least?" We then took that order down. Later we correlated or compared the pupil response order from the biggest pupil response to a food item to the lowest, with the verbal order which they had given to indicate their preference. We tested 64 people and when we compared the pupil ranking with the verbal ranking for each of these individuals, we found that they agreed better than chance for 61 of the people and were equal to chance for only 3. This is a result that, if expected by pure chance, we could get only once in a million times. If we consider that the average psychologist, indeed the average scientist, is perfectly happy to publish a research result which could happen by chance only once in 100 times and in fact will sometimes be satisfied to publish results which could occur by chance 5 times out of 100 times, one can quickly appreciate the tremendous agreement between the pupil and verbal rankings found in this experiment.

But now let us look at the other side of the coin. In another such series we had some photographs which consisted of a female pinup, a male pinup, a mother sitting like Whistler's mother in a rocking chair, an innocuous landscape and several others. There, the agreement between the pupil and verbal rankings was extremely bad. Almost everyone was called upon or felt called upon to place the picture of the mother high in the degree of preference. This was not true for the pupil response. And similarly among women the nude male was rated verbally very low and in most cases last, whereas it elicited a very high pupil response in most of the women subjects. This was not the case for the men, for they verbally placed the female pinup high in their degree of preference and also had a high pupil response. This may be a good indication of the way in which social pressure can work differentially. For example, it is considered on the whole perfectly reasonable for a man to be interested in a picture of a nude female but it is not considered reasonable for girls to be interested in nude male pinups. In fact, it is probably true that in most instances the pictures lining walls in college dormitories of men will largely be nude female pinups and in the case of female dormitories the pictures will be of faces of men or of clothed men. As of this time, however, I would assume this to be changed. Many magazines now show males in all details and I assume they sell.

But there is a good way to test the sensitivity and validity of the pupil response so that we can say with assurance that it reflects differences in attitudes toward what is being shown. Here, we do what every psychologist when doing an experiment with animals must do. For example, in animal experiments it is obviously impossible to determine by asking a question, which of two stimuli or several stimuli is preferred. What is done is to change the motivation of the animal in an experimental fashion so that the way in which the organism will perceive the situation will be affected. In simple words: if an animal will press a lever to get food more often when it is hungry than when it is not hungry, the psychologist makes the simple assumption that the greater work expenditure is a result of an increased desire for food or an increased attractiveness of food. The experimenter says to himself that the attitude toward food, that is, the positive attitude toward food, increases with the amount of hunger drive which he can produce in the organism. If it were not possible to make this sort of assumption, almost all of the research now carried out by thousands upon thousands of psychologists in their innumerable animal experiments would be completely useless.

We thought of testing such a notion with humans and using the pupil response in relation to food pictures and different states of "food deprivation." We tested a number of men and women before lunch who should be, we assumed, hungrier than the other individuals who were tested after lunch. The results were clear and unequivocal. The pupil response for the subjects tested just before lunch was almost three times greater in terms of pupil dilation than those who were considered to be not hungry. It is interesting to note even here that some of the individuals who had very substantial pupil diameter increases, tested before lunch and presumed to be hungry, denied being hungry when they were verbally interviewed after being shown the food pictures. In at least two instances it turned out that these individuals were on a diet and were probably trying to tell themselves that they "really were not very hungry." In a way, then, this particular food test serves to indicate two things: the basic validity and truth that is involved in pupillometrics and the way in which social pressures and other factors can influence and cause rationalization on the part of an individual so that we really cannot trust his responses when given verbally or in some other voluntary way.

**6**

# A Breakthrough— Measuring Attitude Change

Up to the present time we have been talking about measuring interest in or positive attitudes to pictorial material which is presented to the subject. Thus we can get measures of attitudes which relate to the ongoing feelings of the individual being tested. In the preceding chapter we mentioned an experiment in which hungry and non-hungry people were tested in relation to pictures of food. This is a measure of attitude change because we could take the same individuals while they were hungry, expose them to pictures of food, find out their particular response, and then, at a later time, after they had eaten and were satiated, test them on food pictures again. The result would show a change of attitude due to a physiological change in the human.

The measurement of attitude change has long been a problem for the social psychologist. Usually it is accomplished by getting, through interview or questionnaire techniques, some sort of measure of the attitude expressed voluntarily by the subject toward some particular concept, persons or objects. After the experimenter has this information he may expose the subject to situations which he then hopes will cause a measurable change in the attitude. Sometime later an attitude questionnaire or interview is again administered and the results are compared to see whether or not the intervening experience has indeed produced the attitude change which has been postulated by the experimenter.

Let us take one such example. Some years ago a psychologist, by means of interview and questionnaire, determined the attitude of certain individuals, including Southern whites, toward blacks. The questionnaire and interview appeared to indicate a somewhat negative attitude toward blacks. He then had a situation in which the Southern white spent several months working as part of a small team of three people including a black and with a white person who was informed as to the nature of the research. The white person, who had been chosen by the experimenter as a team captain, tried during that time in every way possible to bring out the good points of the black who was working on the team.

At the end of three months, the Southern white who in this case is of course *the* subject was again tested by questionnaire and interview methods and the evaluated results seemed to show a clear increase in positive attitude toward blacks. Now this all sounds very fine and good. The only difficulty is that one has no real assurance that what is reflected here in the so-called change of attitude is real. It could merely mean that this particular individual has an increased positive attitude toward the *particular* black of his work group—something that happens every day because even in those instances where there is bias and prejudice most people will say, "He isn't like the others. He's a good man," and so on.

This kind of information, while it may be meaningful to see whether or not the individual attitude toward that one person is changed, can by no means be interpreted as a basic attitude change toward the group to which the bias and discrimination was directed. While the foregoing experiment has the limitation just mentioned, others are infinitely more difficult to handle. For example, we could ask an individual to rate how he feels about a certain person on a seven-point scale from "dislike very much," "dislike somewhat," and so on all the way to "like very much." We could then expose the subject to some material which gives him additional information about that person. One might very well expect that this information could have a bearing on what the subject will say when again asked to rate that individual on the same scale. This is the usual design of experiments that propose to test for attitude change as a result of information, experience, propaganda, or other attitude changing materials.

It is, of course, involved also in such areas as psychotherapy and advertising. In both cases the experimenter, psychiatrist, psychologist or advertiser tries by one means or another to change the attitude of the individual, usually in a more favorable direction. In the case of psychotherapy the goal is to have the person attain a better outlook, a better understanding of his problems, and a more realistic evaluation of himself and his situation which will make normal living possible. In the case of advertising the attempt is made to increase or change or maintain an attitude toward a product. The measurement of these two processes alone takes up a tremendous amount of the applied research time of thousands of people who work in these areas.

Again, let me make quite clear that such measures of attitude change as have been used are difficult to evaluate, particularly because the subject may very well give the answer which he hopes or feels the experimenter (or society) wants him to give. The literature currently abounds with studies of the influence of experimenter expectation on the results obtained. For example, in a test situation the subjects are asked to rate their attitudes toward a certain product. They are subsequently exposed, in a theatre-like situation, to a number of television commercials which extol the virtues of that product and then they are again asked how they feel about the product. The answer is almost a foregone conclusion. Most individuals feel called upon to go along with the game and rate the product at a somewhat higher level than they did in the previous situation. There have been many and varied ways to get around these difficulties in relation to attitude change. One example will probably suffice. In some of the marketing research, individuals were exposed to a question- naire in which they would rank certain products in the same category, let us say, soap powders. Then in a theatre-like situation, they were exposed to a television show in which several commercials for a particular brand of soap powder were shown. At the end of the session, instead of asking people to rate these products again, they were merely told as they left that each one could take along a box of soap powder.

All of the products which were listed in the first questionnaire were available. Then, by seeing how many of each product were chosen, the experimenters felt that they had an adequate measure of any change of attitude that might have been produced by the exposure to the television commercials shown.

There is a catch to this, though. In some instances, it can be quite clear that the person who chooses a particular product in such a test situation is taking a product for which he himself does not particularly care but which is one that he knows another person uses. He takes the product merely because of the other person's positive attitude toward it. While these examples are from marketing research, the general design of how these kinds of research are carried out is quite the same regardless of whether we are dealing with a social psychology situation or one in which marketing and advertising are involved.

In the research work we have been doing for the past nine years it seemed to me that the greatest usefulness of the pupil response as an objective measure might be for just such *attitude change* investigations. My line of thought was that if the pupil response had the sensitivity and the validity that seemed to be indicated by the hungry versus non-hungry study, then the momentary attitude and interest of the individual would be reflected equally well when some information had been given to that individual and the pupil test was again carried out. Our first experiment along this line was extremely simple. We obtained two photographs of unknown men. They were shown, without any identification, to a number of subjects. One-half of the subjects was told that person A was really the commandant of the concentration camp at Auschwitz and that person B was an Albert Schweitzer type of man who was working for the good of humanity. For the other half of the subjects, we reversed this information so that B became the commandant and A was the good man. This obviously has to be done in any experiment so that one knows that it is not the appearance of the individual that may be involved in the subsequent response change but, rather, that it is the specific information which is attributed to that individual.

The results showed that the response to the person after having been given this information and then retested increased for the Albert Schweitzer type individual regardless of which picture was shown to the different groups and that the pupil response was less than it had been originally to the individual who was identified as the commandant at Auschwitz. This is the simplest type of experimental procedure. The total experimental time is extremely short—the subject was shown the pictures, then had his head out of the apparatus while he was given this information and then was asked to look at the pictures again. All this takes less than a few minutes. We did not try to ask the person to make a judgment on, say, a seven-point scale, before and after being given this information but it seems to me quite reasonable that, given the social values which we have, we would have predicted a change on the questionnaire in the same direction as we received for the pupil response. In other words, most people know that they should react negatively to the commandant at Auschwitz, regardless of what their actual feelings might be, and we would therefore assume that this would be reflected in the verbal judgment and rating which they would make. These results were encouraging enough to us that we carried out further studies.

Sometime later we carried out an experiment in which we gave somewhat more information. It involved an article in one of the popular magazines about a Hollywood actor. This article rather devastatingly presented a very bad portrayal of the actor. I thought it might be good material for producing a pupil change which would thus indicate a change in attitude. We showed the picture of the actor to a number of subjects. Half of the subjects were allowed to read the article before they were again shown the picture of the actor. The other half of the subjects were shown the picture, allowed to read an equal amount of material which did not relate to the actor, and then were shown the picture again. The results were quite clear. Those who read the negative review gave a much smaller pupil response to the actor when shown the picture the second time as compared to the first. Those who read the non-relevant material gave a slightly greater, but not significantly greater response to the same picture of the actor when shown for the second time as compared to the first. This we consider to be an indication of the persuasiveness of the material and how it could be quantitatively measured, that is, how much of a change we would get on the basis of the material presented.

Obviously one of the important attempts made in the United States, as indeed in every part of the world, is to try to influence people's views of a political candidate. The philosophy actually has quite clearly developed that the more you do, the more money you spend, the more exposure on television and other news media, the greater is the likelihood that more and more people will be swayed and convinced to vote for that candidate to whom you show a favorable attitude. In the 1964 presidential campaign, when Barry Goldwater opposed Lyndon Johnson, I became interested in two aspects of the political scene. One was that it seemed to me that almost everyone I met at the University was anti-Goldwater. At least this was true in terms of their professed statement. While this is not terribly surprising since the University is ordinarily the scene of liberal attitudes, it did seem unusual to me to have such complete unanimity. The second point I thought worth testing was to see whether information which was detrimental to either one candidate or the other could possibly make a difference in the attitude that would be reflected by showing pictures of the candidate to the subject. We therefore carried out the following experiment in the summer of 1964, during the heat of the presidential campaign.

We had as our subjects 34 people (18 men, 16 women) from the University of Chicago and the area around it. They ranged in age from the early twenties to the early forties and all of them told us that they were against Barry Goldwater, the Republican candidate, and for the Democratic incumbent, Lyndon Johnson.

We showed each one twelve pictures, consisting of five of Lyndon Johnson, five of Barry Goldwater, one of John F. Kennedy, and one of Dwight D. Eisenhower. The pictures of the same individual were all different. They were shown in the following order: Johnson (J), Goldwater (G), Kennedy, J, G, G, J, J, G, Eisenhower, J, and G. Then the same set was immediately shown in reverse order.

The subjects were randomly placed into one of three different groups, according to the type of reading material they were then given: Group 1 was given anti-Goldwater political propaganda to read; Group 2 was given anti-Johnson political propaganda to read; and Group 3 was given excerpts from a psychology journal that had no political content. The political propaganda was collected from the newspapers and various popular periodicals. They ran as follows:

## Anti-Johnson material

President Lyndon Johnson repeatedly claims that his administration is an honest and benevolent one. Some facts about Johnson's dealings, however, show a glaring inconsistency between what he says and what he does.

In 1961, according to the *Wall Street Journal*, a real estate company in which Lyndon Johnson owned a 75% interest, bought 5,000 acres of land in a sparsely settled area on the outskirts of overcrowded Austin. Since then large lakes have formed in the area, as water backed up behind federally-built dams converted this land into a highly desirable lakeshore property. The real estate company, due to their "foresight" realized a tremendous profit from the sale of this property. It is pertinent to note that Lyndon Johnson openly claims that he was the congressman chiefly responsible for the government dam-building program in that area.

In addition to building dams, Lyndon Johnson also built the political career of Bobby Baker and remained close to him throughout the period of Baker's unethical dealings. It is hard to conceive that Johnson was so unperceptive as to not realize the nature of Baker's activities and one can conclude, therefore, that Johnson gave at least tacit consent to them.

It is well known that Mrs. Lyndon Johnson has built up a vast empire of radio and TV stations, but her methods in this empire-building are not so well known. Lady Bird opened the first radio station in Austin in 1943. Several years later, a long time friend of Lyndon Johnson opened a radio station, which by strange coincidence, had its facilities in the same small house which housed Mrs. Johnson's station. For many years these stations monopolized radio broadcasting in Austin. FCC laws prohibit the ownership of more than one station in a given city, yet although the Johnsons did not violate these laws, the circumstances make it apparent that they controlled both stations in the Texas capital at a time when LBJ was beginning his political career in that state.

In speaking for the Civil Rights Act, President Johnson neglected to note that he owns a large tract of land in Georgia on which many Negro families work and live in a state of poverty and seeming destitution. A *New York Herald Tribune* editorial (March, 1964) referred to this situation as, "one little better than slavery."

Thus, in his personal dealings, Lyndon Johnson risks "conflict of interest" in an unethical, if not in a dishonest manner and indicates that many of his pious statements are backed by some "not-so-pious" actions.

## Anti-Goldwater material

Barry Goldwater's famous "extremism" quote has been followed by his evasive interpretations of this term and a repeated refusal to disavow or condemn any extremist organization. The full meaning of Goldwater's coalition with extremists cannot be appreciated until several hard cold facts about his life and campaign are examined.

On a TV program ("Issues and Answers"; April 7, 1963) Goldwater said, "I don't object to a dictatorship because I realize that not all people in this world are ready for democratic processes. If they have a dictator in order to keep Communism out, then I don't think we can object to that." Advocating a dictatorship to thwart a "Communist threat" is exactly the position taken by Mussolini in WW II Italy. An American citizen need only to consider the horrors and atrocities suffered by the Italians under such a "non-objectionable" dictatorship to realize the possible consequences of electing the holder of such a view to the presidency.

Ken Courtney, head of the *Independent Americans for Goldwater*, is an active member of the Louisiana White Citizens Council and has stated that if the U. S. severed relations with the Soviet Union, "the whole civil rights movement would die on the vine." The implication of this remark is that the Negro struggle for freedom in this country is Communist inspired.

Karl Hess, the ghost-writer of Goldwater's acceptance speech, is a former editor of *Counter Attack*, a magazine which was instrumental in bringing about the blacklisting of many actors, directors and writers for alleged Communist affiliations. He was a contributing editor of *American Mercury* which is known as a bitterly anti-Semitic magazine.

In addition to Neo-Fascists, Ku Klux Klansmen, White Citizens Council members and anti-Semites, Goldwater claims as one of his supporters Robert Welch, the founder of the John Birch Society and the granddaddy of all extremists. This man, a diagnosed paranoic who has condemned Dwight Eisenhower, John Foster Dulles and Nelson Rockefeller as, "tools of a Communist conspiracy" openly brags that he is an active supporter and fund-raiser for Goldwater's campaign.

By refusing to disavow at least some forms of extremism, Barry Goldwater has openly solicited the support of dangerous fanatics such as those described above. It is not the Negro, Jew or Socialist who must fear Goldwater and his supporters—rather it is all Americans, since, as Dick

Gregory puts it, "If Goldwater gets elected in November and Khrushchev makes him mad, ain't none of us gonna have no civil rights."

After reading the indicated material, the subjects were again shown the twelve pictures as before, in the forward and reverse orders. Lastly, the subjects were asked to rate the five Johnson pictures and the five Goldwater pictures as to how representative they thought each picture was of the political candidate. While some of the results which we are going to discuss are based on the initial response to all ten of the pictures, most of them are based on data obtained from the three pictures of Johnson and the three pictures of Goldwater that were thought to be most representative.

There was high agreement between the subjects' verbal responses as to which pictures best represented the candidates and their pupil responses to the pictures.

There were basic differences in the initial responses of the men and the women toward the pictures. According to the data from the three most representative pictures, both men and women had a higher positive response to Johnson than they did to Goldwater. In addition, the women had a higher response to Johnson than men did, and only a very slightly higher responsiveness to Goldwater than the men did. But the photograph of Eisenhower received the highest positive pupil response from both men and women. In fact, pooling the responses of the subjects of both sexes to the four political figures, Eisenhower comes out on top with Johnson second and Goldwater and Kennedy at about the same level. The overall response to Eisenhower is significantly higher than the response to the others.

The effects of the political propaganda on the pupil response of the subjects to the political figures were different between the men and the women. Since the responses of the women seemed variable, we will for the present confine our remarks to the results obtained with men.

With the nonpolitical information group, the men showed virtually no changes in their pupil responses toward the pictures of Johnson and of Goldwater. But the effect of the political propaganda was very different. After reading anti-Johnson material the men's pupils showed a drop in response to Johnson and an increase in response to Goldwater. With the men who read

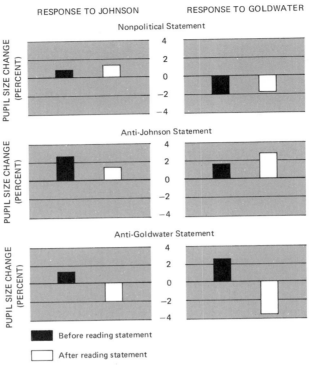

the anti-Goldwater material, however, there was a drop in response to *both* Goldwater and Johnson. The Goldwater response showed the biggest change.

Interestingly, the negative effect of the anti-Goldwater political reading matter was also evident in the subjects' responses to Eisenhower, where the initial responses had been 5.2 per cent and the post-reading response was − .1 per cent. The response to Kennedy, however, remained the same, perhaps because of his assassination, which had occurred less than a year earlier. The anti-Johnson material, however, did not have this kind of effect. The pupil response to Eisenhower remained the same, and there was a slight drop in the response to Kennedy. The nonpolitical reading matter, of course, did not change the responses to Kennedy or to Eisenhower any more than it did the responses to Johnson or Goldwater.

These results, taken as a whole, show that the pupil response not only can differentiate between different political candidates but also between different pictures of the same individual. Information about a political candidate has an effect on the pupil response to the candidate. When this information is biased against the candidate, there is a negative effect on the pupil response of men so that their pupils become smaller. This negative effect also appears to spread and affect the responses to other politicians.

Although all subjects professed to be Johnson supporters and against Goldwater, it was found that about one-third of the subjects had a more positive pupil response to Goldwater than they did to Johnson. While personal appearance certainly could play a role in this, it might possibly be that this indicates more realistically the actual feelings of the group. Even in the liberal atmosphere of the University of Chicago there might be some Goldwater supporters, even though they might not publicly admit it.

Further light upon the political attitudes of people was provided by an additional subsequent experiment which we ran just two months prior to election day. We took the same series of 12 pictures, removed the two photos of Kennedy and Eisenhower, and substituted pictures of nude pinups in their place. The series was shown to seven men. While the response to the Johnson and Goldwater pictures remained at the same level as in the earlier study, −2 and +5 per cent, respectively, the responses to the two nudes were +11 per cent on the average, thus indicating a much greater personal involvement with the nudes than with the political candidates. This result was further confirmed by the GSR readings taken for the seven men while they were looking at the pictures. The GSR deflection for the nudes was ten times greater than that for the political figures.

GSR is a measure of autonomic nervous system activity. Hence the observed GSR deflection indicated that the seven men experienced far greater autonomic nervous system arousal while looking at the nudes than they did while looking at the politicians.

Obviously the pupil response can be very valuable in the study of politics, political beliefs, and the effects of political campaigns. The nonverbal assessment of political attitudes through pupillometrics can aid tremendously in knowing and understanding the emotional dynamics involved.

As I will show later, the ultimate usefulness in advertising and marketing as far as the pupil technique is concerned might well be in such studies which measure the amount of change produced by exposure to some sort of material. One of the first attempts which we made along this line related to showing a half-hour television show which was not yet on TV—a pilot film—to see whether or not any change in attitude toward the title and the actor who played the leading role could be detected as the result of having been exposed to intervening information or material which in this case was a pilot film for a new western. In this experiment we first showed a title for the show superimposed on a suitable western background and then the picture of the leading actor, after which we showed the title of the show again. Half of our group was now exposed to the actual television show for one-half hour and the other half of our subjects merely sat in an adjoining room or looked at magazines during that same period. They were then retested on these photographs showing the title, the actor, and the title again. The results were evaluated and showed a slight but insignificant pupil size increase in the case of seeing no intervening material. On the other hand, those individuals who saw the actual television show had an almost threefold increase in pupil diameter to the same titles and the photograph of the lead actor.

Obviously, if one has followed me in my assumptions regarding what the pupil response shows, this is a clear indication that the show is accomplishing its purpose; that is, it is causing a positive attitude toward the show. One might even go so far as to be able to predict the success of a proposed series when presented on TV if the sample were reasonably representative of television viewers and if the quality of the television show were to hold up in the same way as the pilot film. I shall have more to say about this later when I deal with the problems of the pupil and advertising research.

Now it is reasonable to ask the question of whether we are really dealing with a positive increase in attitude when we get a positive increase in pupil diameter, and whether this reflects a change of such an attitude. There is one kind of experiment which to me has a great deal to say, not only about this particular matter, but also about the nature of the positive and negative components in the pupil response in relation to interest or attitude. This is the result of two studies carried out while subjects were under hypnosis.

The first was done by Kahneman at the University of Michigan and orally reported to me. The subjects were shown two photographs while under hypnosis. These photographs, however, were not actual photographs of material but were really plain gray slides. In both cases, however, they were preceded, as we have always done, by control slides which matched the so-called blank picture slides in brightness. The subject, under hypnosis, was placed in the apparatus and under suggestion was told that he would see two pictures. The first was a very pleasant attractive picture of something that would interest the subject and the second, he was told, would be distasteful and negative to him. The results showed that the slide which the subject could imagine to be a positive or pleasant picture caused a pupil dilation. The second picture which the subject could choose himself since the actual subject matter was not suggested to him but only that this was a negative or unpleasant picture, caused a pupil *constriction*. This experiment, although it was not carried out with any large number of subjects, seems to me a clear indication that what we are measuring is indeed a response to pleasant and unpleasant stimuli and that our big difficulty, as we have previously said in choosing unpleasant pictures for people, is that there is no good way to determine beforehand what material is going to be unpleasant. In this case, however, the choice is left entirely up to the subject and as a result we get a test score that is indicative of the suggested value of the material, although the material itself is not shown.

The next study using hypnosis was done by one of my assistants who first hypnotized a subject and then showed him a series of five food pictures. He subsequently suggested to him that he was getting very hungry. After this suggestion the subject was shown the food pictures again. The pupil increases for the food pictures were now significant. I might add that at the beginning of the test the subject was not hungry. He had eaten breakfast only shortly before the test began. After this subject had made the positive response to the food pictures he was then, still under hypnosis, led through an imaginary meal. The subject himself chose what he wanted to eat. He was told, for example, "Oh, here comes the food, look at the amount. Isn't it tremendous! What is it?" And then the subject would say roast beef and so on until the entire meal was carried out under hypnosis and suggestion. After satiation was suggested, the subject, still under hypnosis, was shown the food pictures again and this time had a *constriction* of the pupils when seeing the food pictures.

In our hypnosis experiment we used only a single individual but I think it demonstrates the precise design for the measurement of material which is used to influence people. Under hypnosis and suggestion we have an almost ideal situation where the information does precisely what it is intended to do and the pupil response makes this clear. With this, we have a definite suggestion that almost any sort of information input can therefore be measured and it makes no difference whether this material is political propaganda, information intended to change persons' attitudes and biases, or even the process of psychotherapy. Let us take a crude example of what might be possible in such a mental health situation.

One of the most difficult things in psychiatric and psychotherapeutic treatment is the assessment of whether or not what the psychiatrist or psychotherapist does is actually achieving its desired objective. It is also often difficult to know whether the psychiatrist or psychotherapist is on the right track in helping the person with his particular problem. In this crude example, let us say that we are faced with an individual who has a great fear of all men with beards. We could take such an individual at the point where he becomes a patient and test him on some photographs which include people with beards and without beards, and thus get a baseline differential in his response to such individuals. Periodically during the course of treatment he could be tested on the same set of pictures. Any change or improvement in his attitude, any lessening of his problem, should then be reflected in the responses which he gives to the individual photographs. Obviously, if this is really possible, and there are some indications that seem to suggest that it is, we would be able to place in the hands of the psychiatric worker an invaluable tool when properly used. One can immediately see that a similar situation would be that involving homosexuality which we previously discussed in relation to the photographs shown to normal and homosexual men. Here too, a change in attitude would obviously be reflected. Actually, such attempts are already in progress by several medical workers to use the technique as a measure of psychotherapeutic effectiveness. One such recent study showed that alcoholics under treatment could be tested "before and after" on olfactory alcoholic stimuli. A prediction of success or failure was later checked by the particular patients who were readmitted.

In the field of mental health it may be quite possible to measure the effectiveness of various types of treatments by the use of this objective measuring technique.

To sum up, the pupil response as a measure of attitude change in an individual has a wide potential in research on social attitudes, clinical and therapeutic procedures, and any other area where the effect of an influence of any sort is to be measured.

# Pupils Can
# Change Pupils

Belladonna is a drug once used by women because they thought it would make them more beautiful. In fact, the word belladonna means beautiful woman. But how did this drug make women appear more beautiful? Actually, belladonna causes the pupils to dilate when placed as drops in the eyes. It is similar to what happens when you go to an ophthalmologist and get a medical eye examination. In order for the physician to be able to see "inside the eyeball," he tries to open the window as much as possible, making the pupil abnormally large by use of atropine or some other substance. As a matter of fact, one of the leading eyewash remedies to make the eyes clear and beautiful, used by women for a long time before the Federal Pure Food and Drug Administration put a stop to it, contained atropine. Now the question is, where did this notion, which has been around for hundreds of years, that larger pupils make a woman look more beautiful and attractive, come from? It is easy to say that obviously this is folklore and can have no scientific basis. I remind the reader of the many medical discoveries which have come from such folklore remedies. For example, digitalis, which is used in the treatment of heart disease was originally obtained from the foxglove plant.

One possible factor in increasing the attractiveness of a woman by pupil enlargement is that this would in effect make her look younger. This is because, as mentioned in Chapter 3, younger people have larger pupils than do older people.

At any rate, this seemed to be a very interesting possibility because my reasoning went as follows. If it is true that the larger pupils which we see in a woman will cause a more positive reaction in a man, then obviously this should be reflected by a similar increase in his pupil size. In other words, seeing bigger pupils causes bigger pupils.

We did an experiment several years ago in which we had two identical photographs as shown in the following illustrations. I took each of these photographs of a young lady and by means of simple retouching changed the pupils in one case, to small, and in the other case, to large. The photographs then looked as you see them in Figures 17 and 18. These photographs, along with a number of other, but neutral, photographs, were shown to over thirty men. For one-half of the men the one with the small pupils was shown earlier in the series, the one with the large pupils later, and this was reversed for the other half of the male subjects. When they were through looking at the pictures, they were asked whether they remembered seeing two pictures of the same girl. Everyone did. They were then asked if they could remember any difference in the way she looked the first time they saw her and then the second time. Almost everyone did and we then asked them what was different about the two photographs. Of course, this question had to be related to the sequence in which the particular experimental subgroup was shown the photographs. *Not one* of the more than thirty male subjects was able to state, at least on a verbal basis, that the pupils of the two photographs were different in size and that this was the only difference. This is a very important result. Some of the individuals, in fact, absolutely insisted that there could have been no difference in the pupil size when they were told that this was the case, and had to be shown the photographs again so that they could be convinced. However, we did get something else on a verbal basis from almost all of the individuals. They did not refer to the photograph of the woman with small pupils as having small pupils but said, instead, that in one photograph (meaning the one with the small pupils) she looked rather cold, selfish, or hard. In the photograph with the large pupils, they reported the woman to be soft, loving, warm, and used other such adjectives. Now, this is actually such a compelling difference when the expression of the face is not too committal that one can easily see this for one's self. If you, for example, find a magazine cover which shows the pupils of a young lady as very small, it is easy to get a second copy of that magazine and with a felt point pen make the pupils in the one photograph considerably larger than in the original. By holding them side by side, one can see the change that this seems to give to the entire face. In fact, a photograph in which it is difficult, from the facial expression, to tell whether or not the person is about to smile or frown, the difference in the pupil size can in itself cause the apparent facial expression to appear either one way or the other.

While it is evident that men are attracted to women with large pupils their responses are generally at a nonverbal level. It seems that what is appealing about large pupils in a woman is that they imply a strong and sexually toned interest in the man she is with, as well as making her look younger, as mentioned earlier. The enlarged pupils, in effect, act as a "signal" transmitted to the other person. Several observations made by others have indicated that this is what really can occur in the interpersonal relationship between a man and a woman, and apparently without conscious awareness.

I have talked to a number of photographers, some of whom have come to our laboratory. They are involved in fashion photography, and after having been shown the differences in some of our sets of photographs, they seemed to be convinced that larger pupils would make the faces which they depicted look better. It is a source of some amusement to look at a newsstand and see that the pupils of some of the female faces on the magazines have been getting larger over the past several years. The reason it amuses me is because those magazines on which the full faces of women appear are almost never directed to men. Magazines directed to men seem to use the full figure much more than the full face, in which case the actual pupil size is not very apparent. We know from our research and that of Thomas M. Simms that women, when looking at pictures of other women, actually get a smaller pupil response and sometimes a constriction when they see a picture of a woman with larger pupils. Of course, magazine covers may show women with large pupils because most fashion photographers are male and thus respond positively to large pupils. We will have more to say about this shortly, when we discuss some of the work done by

**Figure 17**   Photo of a girl whose eye pupils have been retouched to make them quite small.

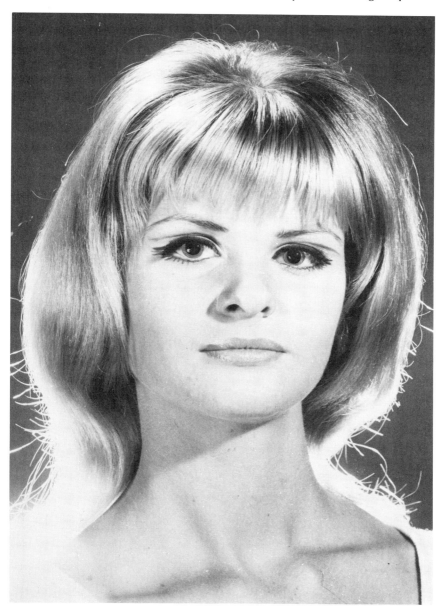

**Figure 18** Photo of the same girl as in Figure 17, but the eye pupils have been retouched to make them quite large. Men normally show a stronger pupil dilation response to a picture of a girl with large pupils than to the same picture with small pupils.

various other investigators on the problem concerning pupil size in pictorially presented faces.

It was not very long after we published some of these findings, and as a result of some lectures which I gave before they were actually published, that some other workers in the field of pupil research carried out studies which extended our findings. The first of these was Thomas M. Simms working at the University of Toronto. In the meantime, however, because of our interest in the ethological concept of the releaser, we had also tried to find out whether or not a purely schematic pair of eyes might elicit responses similar to those elicited by pictures which show actual faces. In ethology it is well known, for example, that a certain part of the total configuration of an animal may in itself be sufficient to produce a behavior change in another animal. A classic example is that described by the ornithologist, David Lack. He found that a robin which will ordinarily attack any intruder, that is, another robin in its own territory, will make this attack not only against another robin but against a mere red feather—which symbolizes the red breast of the robin—placed in an upright position in some strategic spot such as a tree limb. This the ethologists called a *releaser* because it appeared to release some instinctive act and the mere component, red, when it was present, was enough to trigger off the attack response.

In a similar way responses to eye pupils could be innate responses to a specific releaser configuration, or perhaps learned very rapidly in early life. I have concluded this because I have done experiments in which I showed schematic eyespots to people and measured their pupil responses to them. I made up slides showing single, paired, or triple eyespots. These eyespots were made by drawing two concentric circles, and filling in the inner circle to make "pupils." The paired eyespots were placed together to resemble a pair of eyes in a face, and the triple eyespots were positioned in a row the same distance apart as the paired eyespots.

As Tables 4, 5, 6, and 7 show, the subjects who looked at the eyespots had larger pupil sizes in response to the paired eyespots than to either the singleton or triple eyespots. In fact, the subjects had pupil constrictions to the singletons and to the triplets, and pupil dilations to the pairs when responses to the eyespots were averaged together regardless of the size of their "pupils." Responses to the singleton and triple eyespots did not vary systematically in relation to the size of their "pupils." There was no tendency for the pupil responses to be smaller to ones that had small "pupils" or for them to be bigger to ones that had big "pupils." In particular, one would logically expect pupil responses to ones with big "pupils" to be larger simply because of an increased amount of dark area.

**Table 4   Pupil Responses to Single, Double, and Triple Eyespots Regardless of their "Pupil Size"**

|  | O | OO | OOO |
|---|---|---|---|
| Male subjects | − .039 | + .008 | − .056 |
| Female subjects | − .014 | + .022 | − .003 |
| All subjects | − .027 | + .015 | − .030 |

But when the eyespots were *paired,* resembling a pair of eyes in a face, the subjects' average responses to the ones with the smallest "pupils" were the smallest; the responses to the ones with the largest "pupils" were the largest; and the responses to the ones with the medium-sized pupils were in-between. Thus it appears very much as if responses to differences in a person's eye pupils are strongly ingrained if such differences in pupil responses can be obtained to *schematic* eyes.

**Table 5   Pupil Responses to Single Eyespots of Different "Pupil Size"**

|  | ⊙ | ⊙ | ⊙ |
|---|---|---|---|
| Male subjects | − .070 | − .028 | − .020 |
| Female subjects | − .021 | + .004 | − .026 |
| All subjects | − .046 | − .012 | − .023 |

A study by Richard G. Coss in 1965 also used schematic eyes to study pupil responses to pupil size. Concentric circles having solid inner circles of different sizes, were presented in sets of one, two, and three. The group of pictures that consisted of paired eyespots was found, on the average, to cause a greater pupil dilation response than did the groups that consisted of single eyespot or tripled eyespot pictures. The pictures having three eyespots, in fact, produced the smallest pupil dilation in the subjects even though they had a greater amount of dark area than did the single or paired eyespots, a factor which should have served to increase the subjects' pupil sizes.

**Table 6   Pupil Responses to Triple Eyespots of Different "Pupil Size"**

|  | ⊙⊙⊙ | ◉◉◉ | ●●● |
|---|---|---|---|
| Male subjects | −.052 | −.036 | −.080 |
| Female subjects | −.021 | −.008 | +.019 |
| All subjects | −.037 | −.022 | −.031 |

Among the paired eyespots, the one that resembled dilated pupils the most caused the subjects' pupils to dilate much more than did another pair of eyespots which resembled constricted pupils the most. The difference in response to these two sets of paired eyespots was greater in the women subjects than in the men.

Coss's data does not give as great a difference between different size pupils in the double eyespots because he placed

**Table 7   Pupil Responses to Double Eyespots of Different "Pupil Size"**

|  | ⊙⊙ | ◉◉ | ●● |
|---|---|---|---|
| Male subjects | −.008 | +.002 | +.029 |
| Female subjects | +.005 | +.020 | +.042 |
| All subjects | −.002 | +.011 | +.036 |

the schematic eyespots very close together whereas in our study the eyespots were placed in relation to each other as they would be in a normal human face.

Since schematic eyes elicit differential pupil responses it appears that pupil responses to pupil size in another person are innate and not learned. The eyespots are innate schema, just as red spots are for robins. The responses are clearly to *two* eyes rather than just one or three. Research by child psychologists also has shown that babies smile more at schematic faces containing two eyes than at ones containing only one eye, and that even day-old infants are more attentive to a mask with two eyes than with just one.

Thomas M. Simms, inspired by our findings, investigated the pupil responses of men and women, all stably married and therefore presumably heterosexual, to four pictures of a man or a woman, with small or large pupils. He was able to confirm that the men's pupils dilated the most to the picture of the woman with the large pupils. Similarly, the eye pupils of the women dilated most to the picture of the man with large pupils. With both men and women, the dilation to the picture of the person of the opposite sex having the small pupils was much less than the dilation to the large pupils.

Even more interesting, however, were the pupil responses of the men and women to the pictures of their *own* sex. The men's pupils showed almost no increase in pupil size toward either picture of the man. The women, on the other hand, responded to the same degree to the picture of the woman with small pupils as they did to the picture of the man with small pupils. However, their pupil size was even smaller to the picture of the woman with large pupils. This latter fact is congruous with the report of Robert A. Hicks, Tom Reaney, and Lynn Hill that the women they interviewed said that they preferred a picture of a woman who had small pupils rather than a picture of the same woman with large pupils. Thus it is possible that women's magazines will not increase their circulation through the use of large-pupilled women on their covers!

Still other investigators, John W. Stass and Frank N. Willis, Jr., have confirmed that pupil enlargement in a person of the opposite sex increases that person's attractiveness. He introduced people to two different persons of the opposite sex and asked them to pick one of them to be a partner in an experiment. Now one of these people had been given a drug to make the eye pupils quite large and the other had not. Both the men and women were more likely to choose the person who had the large pupils. Stass and Willis also found that eye-contact during the introduction of the subject to the prospective partner was another factor that increased the likelihood of that person being chosen. Furthermore, just as we found in our own work, the subjects were not necessarily able to say that they had used the large-pupil or eye-contact cues as a basis for choosing the partner.

Quana R. Jones and Isaiah S. Moyel have obtained further congruent findings. A picture of a strange male obtained more friendly responses when it had light irises, thus permitting clearer perception of the pupil, than when it had dark irises. Slightly fewer friendly responses were received when the stranger's pupils were large than when they were small.

Taken together, these findings indicate rather strongly, as we suggested in our initial research, that dilated pupils serve as an indicator of sexual interest and, furthermore, indicate that the perception of dilated pupils in a stimulus person, even though not at the conscious level, will arouse a corresponding pupil dilation in an individual who finds this stimulus person's sex membership acceptable. The perception of the acceptable sexual object, with or without dilated pupils, will produce greater pupil response than will the perception of an unacceptable sexual object.

A study with homosexuals, as yet unpublished, was carried out by Thomas M. Simms (personal communication) while he was still at the University of Toronto, and it has further confirmed the notion of the sexual communication value of pupil size. He found that male homosexuals have a distinct preference for a picture of a woman with constricted pupils over a picture of her with dilated pupils. This is still further confirmation of our interpretation of the "signal" value of dilated pupils as an indicator of sexual interest. Interestingly, Simms has observed that men characterized as "Don Juans" also show the same pattern of pupil response to pictures of women as do the homosexuals. Simms has suggested that this indicates that both male homosexuals and Don Juans have an aversion to women whose pupils indicate sexual interest, even though their overt responses to women are apparently very different.

Earlier we mentioned that children have larger absolute pupil sizes than do adults. In light of this, it would seem that having a large pupil size is advantageous to the child since it makes him more appealing to those who take care of him. We believe, in fact, that there has been an evolutionary process which has brought this about; that is to say, there has been a selective process for children to have larger pupils than adults. This is because at his beginning, man did not have social laws that decreed that one must take care of his helpless children. And it is only because early man did indeed care for his children that he has been able to survive as a species for a million years. In order for this to be accomplished the children must have physical characteristics which serve to release parental reactions. Konrad Z. Lorenz has pointed out that in most species there are the same kind of differences in the physical characteristics of the adults and young. And, as we know, animals care for their offspring even though they do not have social customs that require that they do so. Figure 13, shown in Chapter 5 and taken from his article, shows a young rabbit in contrast with an adult hare, a young puppy in contrast with an adult dog, and a young boy in contrast with an adult man. Several features are consistently characteristic of the young, and taken all together they are "babyishness." Limbs are shorter and much heavier in proportion to the torso in babies than in adults. Also, the head is proportionately much larger in relation to the body than is the case with adults. On the face itself, the forehead is more prominent and bulbous. The eyes are large and perhaps located as far down as below the middle of the face because of the large forehead. In addition, the cheeks may be round and protruding. In many species there is also a greater degree of overall fatness in contrast to normal adult bodies.

In the light of Lorenz's postulations, Michael Cann conducted a study that gauged the positive responsiveness of men and women, single and married, parents or childless, to pictures of infant young and adults of several different animal species. These pictures were shown as a series of 53 pairs, each pair consisting of one baby and one adult of the same species, both printed to the same size. It was found that significantly more of the "baby" pictures were preferred over the adult pictures by single women and by childless married women than by single men and childless married men. While women of different ages and marital and parental status tended to show about the same high degree of responsiveness to the pictures of the babies, the responses shown by men tended to increase as a function of marriage and parenthood. The men whose wives were expecting for the first time showed greater responsiveness than did single men; those who had children showed even greater responsiveness. However, the men never exceeded the women in responsiveness.

The status of "babyishness" as a releaser in human beings was confirmed by our initial pupil study in 1960, which also supported Cann's finding of greater responsiveness to babyishness in women than in men. Subsequently we investigated the pupil response of people to progressively stylized drawings of human or animal faces. This stylization was toward greater and greater babyishness in the appearance of the faces, culminating in the Walt Disney-type portrayal of infants and baby animals. Correspondingly greater pupil responses are elicited by greater babyishness, a result which appears to support conclusively the ethological notion that the quality of babyishness definitely has positive appeal to people.

Thus it would seem that our species has evolved so as to have our helpless young possess physical characteristics which enhance their positive attractiveness. There is, it seems, an abundance of such characteristics, not only those described by Lorenz but also the larger pupil size; and all of these combined further the survival of the young through the care of the adults. Furthermore, the evolution has not only been with respect to the characteristics of the young, but also with respect to the adult responsiveness to these characteristics. In other words, for our species to survive the adults must have a built-in positive response to these characteristics. Mankind would perish if adults could not respond to the young, even though they lived in a society which had set up rules that they should.

As with all evolved behaviors and bodily features, there are individual differences in responses to babyishness, even to the extent that there are people who are utterly unable to respond positively to their children although there are social pressures for them to do so. It is the very existence of these few exceptions that show how real the biological basis of parental responsiveness to the young of our species is, because its absence is so surprising and appears so unusual to most of us. Thus it appears that the releaser of babyishness probably has had a high survival value for man. Slobodan B. Petrovich, now at the University of Maryland—Baltimore County, worked with me in the following study of responses to babyishness.

In view of the fact that women generally have much more positive pupil responsiveness to pictures of babies than men do, we decided to find out whether some babies elicit more positive affect than others. We made up a set of six baby pictures which not only included different babies but also three different pictures of the same baby. We showed the pictures in the pupil

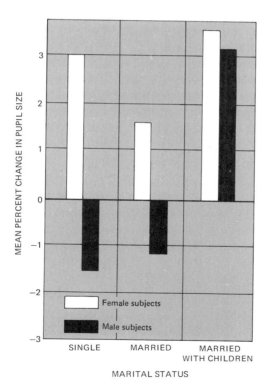

**Figure 19**  Average pupil size response in men and women of different marital and parental status to six baby pictures. All females showed positive responses to the baby pictures whereas only the married men with children did.

apparatus to both men and women of three different marital and parental statuses: single, married with no children, and married with at least two children. These categories were similar to those used by Cann in his study.

As we expected, the women had greater pupil dilations to the baby pictures than the men did. Women of all marital and parental statuses had strong pupil responses to these pictures. Both single and married but childless men generally had negative pupil responses to the baby pictures.

Furthermore, the different faces did elicit consistently different pupil responses among the subjects. One picture was of an apparently autistic baby. Autistic babies are extremely withdrawn children and are unresponsive to other people. This picture elicited pupil constriction responses in all but one of the subjects. Another picture, of a very attractive baby, produced pupil dilation responses in all but one of the subjects, and even in this exception the pupil size remained the same as it had been for the control. Hence this picture did not elicit pupil constriction responses in any subject.

Still another picture of a baby that some subjects interpreted as being about to cry elicited pupil dilation responses in the women subjects and pupil constriction responses in the men subjects. It would seem as if the women's responses were ones of concern for the baby, whereas the men's responses were ones of having been rejected by the baby.

In the light of these findings we concluded that highly attractive babies probably are able to evoke greater interaction from adults in adult-infant social interaction. Again, the fact that babies have large pupils, or respond with enlarging pupils in adult-infant interaction would in general tend to assure at least a minimal degree of the infant-adult interaction that is necessary for the mental and emotional development of the child.

Yet another study we have done further indicates that we have a nonconscious knowledge of pupil enlargement as an indicator of positive responsiveness. The subjects were not tested in the pupil apparatus, but were shown two identical photographs of a mother holding and looking at a baby in her arms. The photograph was so done that both eyes of the mother were visible. In one we had retouched the pupils so that they were quite small.

In the other we had retouched them so they were large. The subjects, students in a class, were asked while shown the photographs in succession, Which mother loves the baby more? The result was unanimous and, as in the previously described experiment, the difference in the pupil response or the difference in the pupil size was apparently not noted until it was later pointed out. All this, it seems to me, points even more to the pupil of the eye as an interpersonal nonverbal communication device.

We have already spoken of the fact that the Chinese jade merchants were astute enough to observe pupil changes when a prospective buyer became interested in their products. Pupil size changes may be clues which are attended to when people face each other and attention to these clues may not necessarily be on a really conscious level. What would happen do you think, if you were to meet someone with blue eyes in which the pupil is easily visible and, as you are introduced, shake hands and look the other person in the eye while he begins to smile at you, you see the pupils of his eyes constrict? We are about to find out. In some preliminary work we have found that it is possible to have a subject in our pupil apparatus look not at a photograph, but at a person who sits directly opposite at arm's length and whose face is almost entirely visible in that part of the apparatus in which photographs are usually projected on a screen. With the screen thus removed the face can be presented to the subject; and the subject asked to look at the right eye of our stimulus person. That person now begins to smile at the subject and at the same time by means of manipulating the light input into the stimulus person's left eye we cause the pupil to constrict. The two attempts at trying to get photographs of the subject's eyes while we were carrying out this particular experiment both ended in failure simply because the subject pulled his head out of the apparatus and refused to look at the stimulus person. We are going to make a serious attempt to investigate the ways in which this interpersonal cue may be used, particularly when the effect of increasing light reflection from the stimulus person's face can be controlled.

All the evidence so far, especially if one looks at the literature which does not deal with scientific work, appears to indicate that such observations may be much more a part of our daily lives than we realize. It also introduces some interesting problems. For example, it is almost impossible even at close range to see the pupil changes in the eyes of Oriental peoples. It is similarly difficult to see such pupils or pupil changes in the eyes of dark pigmented people or people with dark pigmented eyes. It is extremely easy to see these changes in blue-eyed, gray-eyed, or green-eyed individuals. Would it then become reasonable to assume differences in the ability to pick up such interpersonal cues when they are available? Obviously in the case of the card player, in the case of the merchant who wants to transact a sharp deal, or in the case of someone who is trying to convince you of something, it is of consequence to observe the reaction that this will bring out. It is then the poker faced individual who can keep a poker face all the way to his eyes who is obviously going to be at an advantage. He will give away very little information. This is easily possible if one wears dark glasses so that pupillary changes cannot be detected. I have wondered if the "inscrutable Chinese" are inscrutable because of their eye color rather than because of their ability to keep a poker-faced expression.

Some light may be shed by some of our experiments in which I had earlier noted that on the whole, blue-eyed people had larger pupil responses than did brown-eyed people. By this I mean that, with respect to the total range of response from the smallest pupil size for any test series to the largest pupil size, the range was greater for blue-eyed people than it was for brown-eyed individuals. Such a difference was also found by Benjamin Beck who did his Ph.D. dissertation on the effect of sound stimulation on the pupil. He presented clicks of varying frequencies to a sample of blue-eyed men, blue-eyed women, brown-eyed men, and brown-eyed women. He found that the blue-eyed people gave larger pupil responses to sound and that men gave larger pupil responses to sound than did women. Therefore the blue-eyed men gave the largest response and the brown-eyed women gave the smallest response. Others have since rediscovered this finding that blue-eyed people show greater pupil changes.

Some years ago in the development of a color-form test I came across the observation or finding that blue-eyed people were not as color dominant as brown-eyed people. Of course, this is not necessarily the case for every individual; I am speaking now of a *trend* or the average when one takes into account a large number of people. But, one can say that if one has blue eyes then it is more likely that one is form dominant rather than color dominant and the opposite would be true for people with brown eyes. What it basically means is that people with blue eyes tend to pay more attention to form, shape and texture aspects of the world around them although they are certainly able to see color except that it takes a secondary place. In the case of brown-eyed people, there is a greater response to color although obviously form, texture, and shape are also attended to. I devised a color-form test and over many years I did a number of experiments involving almost all of my classes. I found that I was able to show over and over again, almost as a classroom demonstration, that this would be true for any particular sample of people. Actually, I devised this color-form test in 1949, so it has been for 26 years that we have demonstrated this in our classroom as an example of differential perception.

When we discovered the pupil response a few years ago, we decided that one simple experiment might be sufficient to show whether or not there was a greater response on the part of people with blue eyes or brown eyes to colored stimuli, and we conducted the following simple experiment. We used ten people with blue eyes and ten people with brown eyes. The stimuli, instead of being pictures were neutral gray backgrounds, each with a square of one of five colors on it so that each subject first saw a control slide and then a neutral gray background with a patch of color. The colors were shown in succession and were red, orange, yellow, green, and blue. In addition, a white square on a gray background and a black square on a gray background were shown. The total number of stimulus slides shown to each subject was seven. Each stimulus slide, of course, had a corresponding control slide.

Let us first discuss the results of the black and white squares. Obviously enough we were not surprised to find a slightly larger pupil diameter when *all* subjects were looking at the black square as compared to the white one. The results are shown in the following illustration. Similarly, if we look at the responses of the blue-eyed in Figure 20 we find something that is not terribly surprising. We did not control for brightness in any way in this particular case but dealt with pure clear colors. The subjects had the largest response to the blue and to the red, the smallest response to the yellow, and an in-between response to orange and the green. What is most important, however, is to notice that all the responses for the color fall between that response which is for the black and that which is for the white. Since none of the colors is darker than black nor lighter than white this is a reasonable result. In fact, the colors arrange themselves pretty much in terms of what we assume the brightness effect of these colors to be; that is, red and blue would appear darker and closer to black, and yellow would of course appear lighter and closer to white.

But now look at the results in the following graph (Figure 21). This is the effect of color on brown-eyed people. Instead of falling between black and white, the responses to *all* the colors are greater than the response obtained for black. Since this obviously cannot be the result of *brightness,* there must be some sort of excitatory quality or interest which transcends the fact that the brightness of these essentially uninteresting stimuli is greater than would be for black.

We have done a similar study for colored posters which were represented both in full color and also in black and white. For most of the posters it did not make too much difference whether they were in black and white or in color as long as we didn't take into account people's eye color. However, if we separated out the blue-eyed people, we found that their response for the color poster or the representation in black and white was essentially the same for most, if not all of the posters. For the brown-eyed subjects, however, most of the posters in color received larger pupil responses than did those that were in black and white. There was only one subject among the brown-eyed people who was an exception to this general finding. It has been difficult to come to some possible conclusion as to what might be going on when we get these differences between blue- and brown-eyed subjects. I have only one tentative notion regarding this finding. It is that because of the lack of pigmentation in the blue eye there is a greater amount of stray light that enters it through the

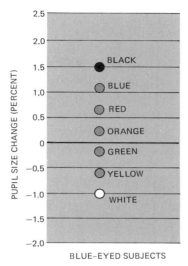

**Figure 20**   Pupil sizes of blue-eyed subjects during the viewing of black, white, and colored squares.

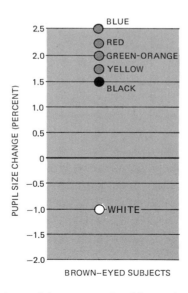

**Figure 21**   Pupil sizes of brown-eyed subjects during the viewing of black, white, and colored squares.

iris, the colored part of the eye itself, and this could have the effect of tending to slightly wash out the full color effect that we see in most instances. It is easy enough to see this sort of effect if one has a slide projector such as one may use at home to show color slides of travel pictures or a motion picture projector to show home movies in color. With the room in almost complete darkness, the colors look fresh, clear, and brilliant. If, however, we turn on a few lights so that there is an increased amount of illumination in the room, perhaps as much as we might ordinarily have if we were sitting in a living room, then the colors on the screen begin to look washed out. In my opinion it is possible that such an effect can result in blue-eyed people having less brilliant colors on their eye retina, therefore not getting color stimulation to the extent possible with brown-eyed people.

This question obviously does not have an easy answer, but in talking about these results as well as my own speculation with individuals conversant with art and decorative products of various groups of people or cultures, it does seem that some elaboration of this whole notion might be worthwhile. Certainly it would be possible in the general area of experimental esthetics to utilize the pupil response in relation to color and form preferences on the part of individuals. I have already mentioned that with modern art, in particular, where often extremely high color is used, the individual responses to specific examples may vary all the way from high positive responses, as in our homosexual subjects, to some individuals who had constrictions which were very great even though they professed or at least persuaded us that they were highly interested in modern art, had copies of paintings on their walls, and lost no opportunity to see exhibits of modern patinting whenever they came to their particular locality.

One of the most interesting speculations from the finding that blue-eyed people have larger pupil responses is that there might actually be some basis to the folk myth that "gentlemen prefer blondes." Blondes are usually blue-eyed and therefore would have more visible pupil responses than brown-eyed women. A man would then be more likely to perceive these pupil changes in a blond girl and thus develop greater positive feelings toward her as a result.

This difference between blue- and brown-eyed people has not been ignored in the literary world. For example, D. H. Lawrence writes of Herman Melville, one of the great authors of stories about the sea, as follows:

He was a modern Viking. There is something curious about real blue-eyed people. They are never quite human, in the good classic sense, human as brown-eyed people are human: the human of the living humus. About a real blue-eyed person there is usually something abstract, elemental. Brown-eyed people are, as it were, like the earth, which is tissue of bygone life, organic, compound. In blue eyes there is sun and rain and abstract, uncreate element, water, ice, air, space, but not humanity. Brown-eyed people are people of the old, old world: *Allzu menschlich.* Blue-eyed people tend to be too keen and abstract.*

It is possible, too, that since it is easier to see the pupil in blue-eyed people than it is in brown-eyed people, that the communicative value of the pupil in social interaction has been maintained during human evolution more in them than it has been in brown-eyed people. Brown-eyed people would then tend to show a greater development of other types of nonverbal communication in social situations, such as hand gestures. The contrast between the "volatile Mediterraneans" and the "cool Nordics" is well known, and has always been thought to be primarily cultural. While we certainly do not wish to disavow cultural influence, there is a real possibility that such temperamental differences have at least some actual biological basis.

As we have shown, the pupil of the eye has probably, along with other biologically derived movements, a great deal of effectiveness in nonverbal communication. It is a field which clearly needs more attention and I shall make some suggestions in the last chapter.

* From D. H. Lawrence, *Studies in Classic American Literature.* New York: T. Seltzer, copyright 1923.

# 8

# Other Senses and Mental Processes

Up to now we have talked exclusively about the pupil responses to visual things, and it may seem to the reader that it is logical that the eye ought to respond only to things which it sees. Actually, as pointed out earlier, this is not the case, and we have seen evidence of this when we looked at the history of pupil research. In reality, anything which causes the brain to react is going to cause a change in pupil size. The pupil just simply is not a stationary, fixed object. When one takes a very close-up motion picture of the eye and then runs the film rapidly—that is, if we do a kind of time lapse photography as is sometimes used with blooming flowers, so that we can actually see the movements of the petals opening by speeding up the time—we can detect the tremendous, erratic changes in the pupil even in a resting condition when there is nothing being shown to the subject. Obviously, as long as his mind is working, changes in the pupil will continue to result even though these changes may be relatively small. I have also mentioned previously the lack of pupil responses of people who are asleep and whose pupils are constricted.

In the sleep laboratory of Dr. Allan Rechtschaffen at the University of Chicago, one of my assistants served as a subject in an experiment for which one eye was taped open during the period when he tried to sleep. At the same time we tried to photograph the eye in order to get some notion of what happens during the time when the person is dreaming. As is now relatively well known, during the period of dreaming a sleeping subject's eyes make rapid movements, and this has been called "rapid eye movement," or REM. During sleep, according to the best evidence we have from a number of researchers, this is the time when dreams occur. Much information in this extremely interesting field has been gathered only during the past several years and it is at the present time a growing research area. Although we have no good experimental data, we do have a clear suggestion in our initial observations that the pupils of the eye dilate during dreaming and that this is concurrent with the rapid eye movements. So, even here it may be possible, although obviously the conditions for experimentation are difficult, to get further insights into the whole process of dreaming—the scientific investigation of which had been left in the hands of armchair speculators for so long.

To return now to the kinds of responses that will occur regardless of the type of stimulation, we might briefly consider the fact that there has been a great amount of work done on what the Russians call the *orienting reflex*. This is a response which is easily noticeable if you happen to have an animal like a cat in the house. If the cat is placidly sitting, staring into space, and suddenly there is a small sound from one corner of the room, the cat will turn its head toward the source of sound with simultaneous pupil dilation. We did something quite similar to this some years ago by showing a hungry cat a dish in which it normally received its food. The accompanying photograph (Figure 22) shows the cat at rest looking into space. The second photograph (Figure 23) shows the same cat a second after the food dish was shown to it. Actually, since it now looked more closely, that is, focused nearer than it did before, the pupils should have gotten even smaller as a result of the accommodation process which we mentioned in an earlier chapter. This was not the case and the pupils increased by a factor of about 400 to 500 per cent in area. We had similar results, although with less pupil dilation, when we worked with hungry dogs.

Dr. Polt, who played a part in the very first experiment which I described in this book, has done further work with cats. He had cats come up to a small window in an experimental apparatus in order to see various things which were on a small stage not far from them. At the same time, by means of a telephoto lens arrangement, he was able to photograph their eyes and to get

**Figure 22** A cat resting and looking out in space, with small eye pupils.

**Figure 23** The same cat, immediately after its food dish was shown to it. As may be seen in comparison with Figure 22, its pupils enlarged considerably.

records of the pupil responses which were produced when they were shown different kinds of material. He was even able to show projected pictures to them. It was with some interest that we noted that a *still picture* of cats would cause a small pupil increase in the cat who was observing the picture, but that a *motion picture* of cats elicited a much greater pupil response. To summarize, then, the pupil will respond to all sorts of mental activity and this is perhaps the reason why it has been so useful and should be useful to an even greater degree in future research.

One of the first areas other than vision to which we turned our attention some years ago was olfacto-gustatory stimulation, that is, taste and smell. It became apparent that contrary to the kinds of responses we were able to obtain with visual material there was no dichotomy, no two-way direction of responses to, say, good taste and bad taste. In fact, something that had essentially no taste might get very little response. Good taste would produce bigger pupils, but so would bad taste.

On the basis of this, we decided to see whether or not it might be possible to take a number of substances in the same general category which differed in taste but which were all on the pleasant side rather than ranging from unpleasant to pleasant. Our first study was carried out with five different commercially available popular orange flavor drinks. Since orange is generally well-liked, people should regard all the flavors as being pleasant, but at the same time have preferences for some of them over others. In order to do this, we had to construct a slightly different version of our apparatus—one which would allow us to have the person sip from containers by means of a straw which, in each case, would be presented to him while he was looking at a control slide. This control slide was the same as that used in our previous visual experiments and the experiment ran essentially as follows.

The subject was seated at the apparatus, given instructions to look steadily at the center of the screen and to hold the straw in his mouth, taking a sip whenever the experimenter said "sip." The liquids were kept in individually coded opaque containers behind the apparatus. When the subject was to take a sip, the experimenter raised the appropriate glass to the straw, held it there for 5 seconds, and then said "sip." After the subject had sipped and swallowed, the glass was removed. Sips of liquid were taken in this fashion every 20 seconds.

The first, and every other sip thereafter, was of plain water. In between these sips of water, one of the orange beverages was presented. The five beverages were presented in a forward order for half of the subjects and in a reverse order for the other half, so as to account for any effect from the order in which the five orange flavors were presented. We tested 4 women and 12 men, all graduate students at the University of Chicago, ranging in age from 24 to 41 years.

Table 8 shows the mean increases in pupil diameter during the sips of water and the sips of orange drinks. The increases in pupil size were determined by first measuring the pupil size during the five seconds before a sip had been taken and then measuring the pupil size during the five seconds immediately after a sip had been taken. The mean pupil size before the sip was then used as the basis for determining the amount of pupil size increase in response to the sip.

**Table 8   Mean Increases in Pupil Size in Response to Five Presentations of Water and to Five Different Orange Flavored Beverages**

| Water | 8.1% | Orange 1 | 5.4% |
|-------|------|----------|------|
| Water | 4.8% | Orange 2 | 3.6% |
| Water | 3.7% | Orange 3 | 10.6% |
| Water | 3.3% | Orange 4 | 5.6% |
| Water | 4.5% | Orange 5 | 3.7% |

As Table 8 shows, there was an increase in the size of the pupil during all of the sips, whether of water or of orange drinks. There also was a definite difference in the responses to the five orange drinks, with the third orange beverage causing the greatest increase in the pupil size. The second and fifth orange beverages, on the other hand, received the lowest pupil responses among the orange drinks and were at the same level as the responses to the last four water sips. Although the overall response to the water sips was 4.9 per cent mean increase in pupil diameter, the first presentation of water elicited a mean response of 8.1 per cent among the 16 subjects. This high response is probably due to the "first stimulus" or novelty effect which we discussed earlier. Therefore, if the first sip of water is discounted because of the novelty effect it appears that successive sips of water are not differentiated by the pupil response, while the sips of orange drinks are.

While there was a slight downward trend in the pupil response to the sips of water, this does not appear to be caused by the taste buds becoming insensitive to the orange or water drinks. Helmut Hahn, Günter Kuckulies, and Harald Taeger have shown that the recovery of the sensitivity of the taste receptors is almost complete within 20 seconds when liquids of this type are used. Rather, this trend is the same one that has been found by the Russian researcher A. E. Liberman, who reported that when he gave the same taste solution for periods of 1½ seconds at 15- to 20-second intervals, there was a tendency for the pupillary dilation orienting reaction to become less and less marked.

Since all the drinks were orange flavored and one orange beverage could be picked out as superior to the others, this appears to indicate that the pupillary response to taste stimuli is extremely sensitive. This conclusion that the third orange beverage was responded to most positively by the subjects was further supported by the fact that when the subjects were asked, after the experiment, to rate the five drinks in order of preference, this particular drink was the one that was rated the highest.

Obviously there is still a great deal of work to be done on the effect of taste on the pupil response, particularly with respect to unpleasant tastes, but it already appears that the pupil response can serve as a technique in studies of how people like food. As will be shown subsequently, it may be possible to separate the positive responses from the negative responses to taste stimuli by means of auxiliary information which can be simultaneously obtained from the subject while he is part of the experimental situation.

Quite the same sort of situation occurred when we worked with smell. A more pleasant smell would create a greater pupil dilation than one which was essentially neutral. But unpleasant smells, particularly very strong, obnoxious, or shocking smells— for example, sudden exposure to ammonia fumes—would cause a great amount of dilation which exceeded that for a pleasant smelling substance such as perfume. But smell, perhaps more than any other stimulus to our senses, is extremely difficult to control. In fact, there is a nearly complete lack of good experimental information in spite of the fact that attempts at classification of odors and experimental research with them has been going on for more than a hundred years. Again, it would seem possible to us that by means of this particular response used in conjunction with others, one could perhaps make a dent into the hitherto rather resistant problem of the nature of smell.

From the very beginning we were interested in the effect of sound on pupil responses. We tried such diverse things as exposing subjects to music of various types, and also to relate their expressed verbal preference to pupil changes in relation to these particular selections. But, on the whole, we have come up with very little useful information that would give us some indication that the pupil response is relevant to this particular area of stimulation.

There are some exceptions, however. One of these is a study mentioned earlier, that was carried out by some students at the University of Chicago in which they exposed the subjects to pre-taped baby cries. These cries were of three kinds: one was a babbling sound of a baby when it apparently was contented, another was a hunger cry, and a third was a pain cry. The tapes were obtained from a psychiatrist in Boston. The experimental procedure was as follows. The subject first heard a neutral tone for ten seconds, then one of the cries, then another neutral tone, and so on. The sounds were repeated twice, but in different order. In this way, then, it was similar to the presentation of pictures. With this particular arrangement I also carried out a small study using only ten subjects but using a pupillometer which had been loaned to me by Bausch and Lomb and which allowed us to get immediate information as to pupil changes on the part of the subject. To my astonishment, for the first time in our research using sound we now had negative responses. In fact, in the several instances where we had the most negative responses, that is, the greatest amount of constriction as compared to the preceding neutral tone, this response was to the cry of the baby in pain whereas in all cases the response to the babbling of the baby was that of dilation. Again, we have to consider this experiment as exploratory, but it does suggest the possibility that with the proper procedure, it may be possible to deal with affect value, that is, both positive and negative responses to different sounds.

In further experiments, we were able to show quite distinct differences when the subject was asked to feel or touch various textured materials. These ranged from something as unpleasant as sandpaper, to smooth material, soft and velvety material, or smooth hard material. Again, the results in this exploratory research were clear. Differences in response did exist and may allow us to get information about the meaningfulness of this sort of sensory input.

In another study we investigated the effects of pain in relation to pupil response and here the results in general confirmed what had been known for a long time. That is, in most cases the pupil dilates when pain is received. The pain in one of our experiments consisted of doing to the person that which had to be done anyway. We set up the pupil apparatus in the clinic of the University of Chicago Hospital where the health service was taking blood samples of their patients by means of a small lancet device which pricked the finger in order to extract a drop or two of blood. What was interesting, however, was that we did not get a pupil dilation response in all cases. Again, there are possibilities for further research. The subject of pain is one of the least understood and most philosophized about aspects of the human experience.

One other experimental procedure was used by us and it is a procedure which certainly relates to pain. While placed in the apparatus and looking at a control slide, a subject was asked to put his hand into a bucket of ice water. After a short interval the hand feels as though a vise is clamped around it and certainly I, while being a subject, found this experience extremely painful. Again there was no precise correlation in terms of a pupil dilation between this painful experience and that of placing the hand, say, in water of body temperature. It may be that this differential response to pain-producing stimuli could be of value in the personality assessment of individuals.

The effect of work and effort, the effect of anticipation of stimuli and other phenomena have been studied by other investigators. One of the more recent studies is the work by Jum C. Nunnally, Paul D. Knott, Albert Duchnoski, and Ronald K. Parker, who assessed the quantitative effects of lifting three different iron weights (10, 20 and 30 pounds) upon pupil size. The phenomenon of muscular effort increasing pupil size was, as we mentioned earlier, well known in the German literature at the turn of this century. Each one of the male subjects was asked to lift one of the weights to a height of one foot for a period of ten seconds and then to rest for ten seconds before lifting another weight. The weights were lifted in an order of increasing heaviness and then of decreasing heaviness, so that there were five lifting trials. As the weights increased, there was an increase in the pupil size during the lifting. During the intervening rest periods the pupil size, though smaller than that for the just lifted weight, was nevertheless larger than the dilation for the weight that had been lifted prior to that weight. As the weights decreased, the pupil size during the lifting periods also decreased, with the resting pupil sizes following suit but being slightly larger than the size for the next weight lifting period. In all cases, however, the resting pupil size was only slightly larger than for the next weight lifting period. It was, of course, much smaller than for the weight lifting that preceded it.

Ronald K. Parker and Robert S. Mogyorosy, enlarging on the above study, used ten men as subjects and four weights, 10, 20, 30, and 40 pounds. Each subject lifted the weights as in the first experiment; for ten seconds each and to a height of one foot, with ten-second resting periods. However, the weights were presented in a random, nonsystematic order. In addition, each subject was tested on two different days. It was found that the heavier the weight, the larger the pupil size during the weight lifting. Isometric exercises such as fist clenching were also performed by the subjects and found to result in pupil dilation.

Jum C. Nunnally and his associates have also found that other kinds of arousal or stimulation can cause pupil dilation in people. One of the most interesting of these was the pupil responses of people who expected to hear a gunshot. One experimenter put blank cartridges in a .22 caliber pistol in view of the subject, while the other gave instructions on how to look at the numbers that would be projected on the screen of the perception apparatus. The subject was told that the numerals 1, 2, 3, 4, and 5 would twice appear in that order for ten seconds each on the screen and that while the numeral 3 was on the screen the gun might be fired. It would be fired, if at all, only when the 3 was on. The sound of the gunshot was then demonstrated. The subject was given two minutes to "settle down" from the gunshot. While the gun was never shot during either of the showings of the five numerals, the subject's pupils increased very rapidly to a peak level at the numeral 3 during both showings, with the peak at the second sequence slightly lower than during the first sequence, and a sharp dropping off during the next two numerals.

Anticipation of difficult problems to be solved will cause slight increases in pupil size, as we have already mentioned. As cited in Chapter 3, it was also observed by German researchers at the turn of the century that even thinking of performing muscular exertion will cause eye pupils to increase in size. Other kinds of anticipation, such as expecting to see an erotic picture of a girl, will also produce considerable pupil dilation, as we found in our own laboratory. In fact, the dilation so produced would often be even greater than that which we usually find for pinup pictures from popular men's magazines! Again, this is an area almost completely untouched by good research and our hope is that there will be some investigators who will devote their skills to this problem.

# 9

# Other Mental Processes

We have already mentioned in the historical chapter that it was discovered late last century that the pupils of the eye dilated when subjects were asked to solve mental arithmetic problems. It was pointed out that no degree of quantification was used but merely the fact that the pupils do get bigger was noted in relation to doing such mental work.

Before we actually became familiar with this historical material (it is not too readily available to the psychologist of today), we independently carried out an experiment on mental arithmetic. Fortunately for us, however, before we sent our manuscript to the publisher we did do a thorough search of the literature and came up with the references which dealt with these earlier observations. Still, it seemed worthwhile for us to publish this material because we were dealing now with a *quantification* of this material and were really able to distinguish problems that were easier and that were harder. In addition, we were the first to record and demonstrate the moment-to-moment changes in pupil size during mental processing. We carried out this study in a rather simple way, using only five subjects because the results we obtained seemed so clear-cut that it seemed senseless to merely continue gathering more and more data. The experiment and the results were as follows.

We gave simple mathematical problems to our subjects to solve. By using the pupil apparatus and the frame counter attached to the camera motor, we were able to determine the exact changes in the pupil size as well as the precise moment at which they occurred.

Four men and one woman were used in this study. They were all people of presumably above average intelligence, since we had a Doctor of Philosophy, two college graduates working for an advanced degree, a college graduate, and an undergraduate research assistant in the psychology department of the University of Chicago.

Each subject was asked to look steadily at the numeral 5 in the middle of a projection screen, approximately 1.45 meters away from him. They were told that they would be given math problems to solve in their heads and that they were to give their answers orally when the solutions had been reached.

One experimenter operated the camera while another gave the instructions and told the subject whether or not the answer was correct. A third experimenter noted from the frame counter attached to the camera the number at which the questions were posed and answered. The subject was given half a minute to adapt to the experimental situation before any problems were given. In addition, five to ten seconds elapsed after the answer was given before the next problem was posed.

All problems were given in the same order to each subject: first, multiply 7 by 8, then multiply 8 by 13, then 13 by 14, and lastly, 16 by 23. Since there is sometimes a tendency for later portions of an experiment to cause smaller pupil responses than the earlier portions, giving the problems in order of increasing difficulty would help to balance out such an effect. If any adaptation to the experimental situation did occur, it would have the effect of making the differences in the pupil responses to the problems smaller rather than larger.

The results which we obtained were obviously clear enough to allow us to rank problems in their order of difficulty. In the individual analysis of some of the material, the fact that after each problem was solved and the answer given, the pupil size returned to its normal level or baseline became apparent, and can be clearly noted from the graph. This in itself is interesting enough because it seems as though the pupil gets bigger and bigger as the person works on the solution to this simple arithmetic problem; then, having reached it *and* given the answer, it is almost as though he has unloaded himself of a heavy weight and the pupil goes back again to its normal size for the amount of illumination which is present in the experimental situation. This "loading" and "unloading" has also been the subject of work carried out by other researchers and we will deal with it shortly.

Of even greater interest to me was the finding that is shown in the last problem solution of this particular subject where one can see clearly a peak of pupil dilation as the problem is attacked, a decrease in pupil size for a short period of time, another peak, and only then the actual drop back to the baseline. I was puzzled as to what this could mean. By talking to the subject who had given us this pupil response I learned that he seemed to remember quite clearly having solved the problem very quickly but being uncertain of the answer, thought that before he made a fool of himself in giving the wrong answer he would recalculate the problem. Only at that point, when he had recalculated it and was sure, as evidenced by that final peak, did he give us the response. Then, of course, the pupil returned immediately to its normal size.

This certainly opened up a possibility that I hadn't considered before. Why couldn't we use the pupil response in determining who is better and who is worse in what we would call decision-making? There it is not only the matter of how long it takes to make the decision or whether or not all decisions are accurate but also whether or not the person is capable of coming to a conclusion systematically, reasonably quickly, without having the kind of self-doubt which causes the decision-making process to be carried out several times instead of the one necessary event. In other words, even with such a simple problem as multiplying two numbers and coming up with the answer, we could separate the people who would be doubtful of what they had just done, sometimes repeating the process three times before actually giving the answer. It does not necessarily mean that the amount of time was much greater than that used by someone else to arrive at the same conclusion in a single process. It merely means that here is a distinct difference in people in the way in which they handle a small decision-making problem.

It seems to me that it would certainly be possible to determine the decision-making ability in people and, there is some evi-

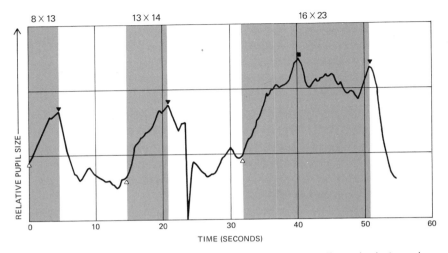

**Figure 24** Sequential pupil sizes in a subject mentally calculating three different multiplication problems are shown here. In each case, as soon as the problem was given (shown by the open triangles), the pupil increased in size until the solution was reached and the answer given (shown by the solid black triangles). After the answer was given, the pupil went back to the size normal for the illumination level. In the case of the third problem, the subject arrived at an answer, as shown by the solid square, and then recalculated it. Upon arriving at the answer the second time the subject reported it, after which the pupil went back to the control level. (From Hess, E. H., Attitude and pupil size. *Scientific American,* **212,** No. 4, 46–54 (1965). Copyright ℗ 1965 by Scientific American, Inc. All rights reserved.)

dence that this can be done on the basis of already performed experiments. For example, problems could be set up in an experimental situation for executives or potential executives where their ongoing mental processes in the solution of the problems can be studied and evaluated not only in terms of the kinds of conclusions which come out or the length of time but also what is actually going on inside the head in relation to certainty or doubt. We have also found that this is quite possible with the use of anagrams rather than by means of simple arithmetic problems. Here again we can follow the course of the mental processes which go on while the person is seeking the solution and we know the point of solution even if the subject does not volunteer this information. In other words, what happens in a situation where the subject has the answer is that there is a drop from a peak. It does not, however, allow the pupil to go all the way down to its normal, pre-problem level. It is as though there is some mental effort to hold that solution but this mental effort is not as great as the amount of effort that was needed to get at that solution. The subject is still carrying part of a load. This is reflected in the larger pupil size which can only go back to its normal level when the system has been completely unloaded.

**Table 9   Percentage of Increase in Pupil Diameter at the Point of Solution of a Problem as Compared with the Diameter of the Pupil before the Problem was Posed**

| Subject | Problem | | | |
|---|---|---|---|---|
| | 7 × 8 | 8 × 13 | 13 × 14 | 16 × 23 |
| H.H. | 15.2 | 15.8 | 20.2 | 22.9 |
| E.K. | 9.8 | 14.1 | 24.9 | 21.2 |
| T.H. | 10 | 8.9 | 13.5 | 23.1 |
| G.B. | 4 | 8.8 | 7.8 | 11.6 |
| P.M. | 16.2 | 9.1 | 25.1 | 29.5 |
| Mean | 10.8 | 11.3 | 18.3 | 21.6 |

From Hess, E. H. and Polt, J. M. *Science*, Fig. 1, **143,** 1190–1192 (13 March 1964). Copyright 1964, by the American Association for the Advancement of Science.

The *degree* of the load also appears to be indicated by our study on mental arithmetic. When we took the average size of the pupil of a subject during the 2½ seconds immediately before a question was asked and compared it with the average size of the pupil during the 2½ seconds immediately before the answer was reported, we found that the increases in pupil size ranged from 4 to 29.5 per cent. Table 9 shows the scores of the individual subjects for each of the problems. While there is not a perfect agreement between how much the pupil dilated during problem solving and the difficulty of the problem in the case of individual subjects, there is complete correlation between the difficulty of the problems and the mean responses of the five subjects. In all cases of non-agreement for the individual subjects, the reversals are between two problems adjacent to each other in difficulty, such as between problems 1 and 2, 2 and 3, or 3 and 4.

The degree to which the pupils dilated during problem solving and the amount of time it took to solve the problem suggests that we could postulate that "total mental processing load" is being measured by a combination of both of these measures, very much as Jacques Roubinovitch suggested at the turn of the century.

Here, then, we find that the pupil dilation can indicate the difficulty of the problem-solving situation. We designed this experiment to eliminate any pressures, sense of competition, or anxiety on the part of the subjects. We feel that we did eliminate these factors because other preliminary research we did in which the subject mentally posed his own problems and answered them himself disclosed the same pattern of pupil response.

Since it might be thought that the increase in pupil size could be due to changing the focus of the eye during the mental calculations, we tested subjects for such effects by having them look alternately at an object very near to the eye and one farther away, about three meters from them. Such changes in focusing caused an average increase of about 2.1 per cent in the pupil size. As we know from Heinrich's work, the changes in pupil size due to mental calculations are readily observable whether the subject is looking at a near object or at one far away.

In our experimental situation, too, the voice of the experimenter giving the problems to the subjects did not affect, in itself, their pupil size. Had this been the case, there should have been a regular and immediate increase in pupil size when each problem was presented. However, the pupil size increased slowly (and occasionally even went down) from the point at which the question was asked, and reached a peak immediately before the solution was given anywhere from 3 to 30 seconds later.

Electroencephalographic measurements have been taken during problem solving of this type by Stanley Lorens and Chester Darrow. They reported that there was a significant increase in alpha brain waves recorded at the back of the head. These changes in brain waves are regarded by scientists to indicate increased activity in the parts of the brain having to do with association processes. They found an "on-off" effect in the brain wave activity which occurred when the subjects had solved the problem. This occurred regardless of how difficult the problem was. With the pupil response, however, we are not only able to determine when the problem was solved but also how difficult the problem was for the subjects.

Other exploratory experimentation which we have carried out on the pupil behavior during mental problem solving has confirmed the earlier findings of Roubinovitch on other points. For example, subjects who find a problem very easy show little change in pupil dilation. On the other hand, when a subject feels that it is impossible for him to solve a problem, pupil dilation will fail to occur because he will not exert any mental effort to attempt to solve it.

This sort of research might also have some interesting implications for education. For example, it is not inconceivable to me that it would be possible to teach different methods of, say, mathematical problem solving and then have the students tested while the problems are being solved. By plotting out the pupil changes which occur during the problem solving, it would be possible to determine the number of steps necessary to solve the problems because each step will have a peak. Also, the magnitude of the actual pupil change would denote the difficulty in terms of the greater or lesser amount of mental effort that goes into the solution of the particular problem. Research on this sort of mental process has been progressing at a rapid pace in a variety of research institutions, and much of it has confirmed our findings.

One such study is an investigation conducted by Dr. James Polt after he went to teach at Temple Buell College. The purpose of this study was to determine the effect of introducing anxiety in the form of a threatened shock for an incorrect answer into a mental problem-solving situation, and to compare individual responses with other indices such as College Board scores and classroom performance.

The subjects were 14 freshmen women, 18 and 19 years old. The experiment was conducted in two sessions, separated by three weeks. The purpose of the first session was to obtain baseline levels of pupil size for each subject and to acquaint the subject with the apparatus and procedures before the actual experiment was begun. During this session the subject fixated on a point on the screen for two minutes while one frame of film was taken per second. The mean pupil size during the last 20 frames was used as the subject's baseline. Each subject was then randomly assigned to the experimental or control group, after which the appropriate subject shifts were made to equalize the mean baseline level of each group.

During the second session, each subject was given two series of three multiplication problems. In each series the problems progressed in difficulty from the first to the third. Each subject was told that she was to mentally solve a set of multiplication problems, using whatever amount of time was required, and to give the answer orally when the solution to each was reached. After a five-minute rest period following the first series of problems, an electrode wired to a shock box was taped to the wrist of the subjects in Group I. The subject was told that she would be given another series of problems, that she was to respond as before, but that this time she would be shocked for an incorrect answer. Subjects in Group II were merely told that they would be given another series of problems, and to respond as they had on the first series. Although subjects in Group I were threatened with shock, no shocks were actually given because of the possible disruptive effect the shock might have on the pupil response. Subjects were not told if their answers were correct or not.

The changes in pupil size shown in Table 10 reflect the per cent difference between the mean pupil size for the five frames immediately before the problem was presented and the five frames bracketing the frame on which the answer was given; that is, two frames before the answer frame, and two frames after the answer was verbalized.

In Series 1, both groups of subjects demonstrated pupil dilation during problem solving (see Table 10). The response was significantly higher to the third problem than to the first problem in Series 1, reflecting the greater difficulty of the third problem. While dilation was seen to be consistently greater in Group II than in Group I in Series 1, the difference was not statistically significant.

With the second series of problems, the differences in magnitude of dilation between problems one and three were again significant for both groups, supporting our earlier findings. In contrast to Series 1, there was a statistically significant difference in the amount of dilation to all three problems in Series 2 between the two groups. This reflects the effect of the shock threat, without which pupil dilation during problem solving decreases as the subject becomes adjusted to the entire situation (as shown by Group II) and the "response set" permits more

**Table 10  Mean Control Pupil Diameter, Mean Peak Pupil Diameter During Problem Solving and Mean Per Cent Increase in Pupil Diameter During Problem Solving**

| | Series 1 | | | | | | | | |
| | Problem 1: 9 × 12 | | | Problem 2: 12 × 13 | | | Problem 3: 13 × 17 | | |
| Group | Mean Control Pupil | Mean Peak Pupil | Mean Per Cent Increase | Mean Control Pupil | Mean Peak Pupil | Mean Per Cent Increase | Mean Control Pupil | Mean Peak Pupil | Mean Per Cent Increase |
|---|---|---|---|---|---|---|---|---|---|
| I | 67.4 | 75.5 | 12 | 71.8 | 82.7 | 15.1 | 70.3 | 83.7 | 19 |
| II | 66.8 | 74.1 | 10.9 | 69.6 | 78 | 12.1 | 67.8 | 79.7 | 17.6 |

| | Series 2 | | | | | | | | |
| | Problem 1: 8 × 13 | | | Problem 2: 11 × 21 | | | Problem 3: 14 × 18 | | |
| Group | Mean Control Pupil | Mean Peak Pupil | Mean Per Cent Increase | Mean Control Pupil | Mean Peak Pupil | Mean Per Cent Increase | Mean Control Pupil | Mean Peak Pupil | Mean Per Cent Increase |
|---|---|---|---|---|---|---|---|---|---|
| I | 67.6 | 72.5 | 7.3 | 70.1 | 78.2 | 11.6 | 67.4 | 76.3 | 13.2 |
| II | 67.2 | 76.7 | 14.1 | 73.4 | 86.8 | 18.3 | 71.1 | 87.4 | 22.9 |

NOTE: Mean pupil diameters (in millimeters) reflect a 17.5 magnification of the image of the eye. Each mean represents the measurement of five consecutive control pupils or of five consecutive pupils during problem solving for each subject.
(From Polt, J. M. Effect of threat of shock on pupillary response in a problem-solving situation. *Perceptual and Motor Skills,* **31,** 590 (1970). Reprinted with permission of author and publisher.)

efficient use of effort to solve the problems. It is of great importance to note that the pupillary dilation caused by anxiety increased during the *problem-solving* phase rather than during the *control* phase.

This finding would suggest that the anticipation of a potentially unpleasant event does not in itself activate the physiological response of pupillary dilation, but sets up a triggering mechanism for the pupillary dilations. This triggering can be produced by an event associated with the unpleasant experience. That is, there is a heightened sensitivity to certain aspects of the environment and this heightened sensitivity produces an enhanced response to pupil dilation during certain relevant conditions.

In this study the threat of shock did not result in a continuously elevated level of pupil dilation, but to greater dilation responses during problem solving, where an incorrect answer had been associated with shock through the instructions. The problem triggered the anxiety response even though the shock, which would itself produce dilation, was never experienced by the subject. The increases in dilation responses shown by Group I subjects in Series 2 did not alter the relationship between pupillary dilation and problem difficulty. Apparently the contribution of mental effort and activation had an essentially additive effect in producing the final pupil response.

Correlations were done between five measures: pupil dilation response during problem solving, amount of time to announce the problem answer, College Board mathematical aptitude scores, College Board verbal aptitude scores, and freshman year grade point average. The pupil response and latency measures are for the 14 subjects in both groups for the first series only, when conditions were the same for both groups. Both the pupil and latency scores were mean scores for the three problems in Series 1. The lowest pupil score and quickest problem-solving score were given a rank of "1," while the highest scores in the other three categories were given the rank of "1." The only significant correlation was between pupil dilation and College Board mathematical aptitude scores. That is, there was a significant relationship between low pupil dilation indicative of less effort and higher mathematical aptitude.

The results suggest that one possible application of the pupil technique would be in the measurement of aptitude. Further validation studies would be necessary before any concrete steps could be taken in this direction, but there is an indication from these data that the response during mental problem solving is related to at least one objective measure of aptitude, the College Board mathematical aptitude score. While the correlation between the pupil response and an objective measure of performance, grade point average, is in the positive direction, this correlation was not significant, probably because the grade point average was not solely concerned with performance in mathematics.

A great deal of further research on pupil manifestations of mental activity has been done by Daniel Kahneman. Kahneman came to our laboratory shortly after we had done the initial mental arithmetic research. He was intrigued with it and we gave him the information necessary for him to set up his own pupil research laboratory at the University of Michigan. The first of his published papers was with Jackson Beatty and appeared in 1966. Among other things, they had their women subjects do the following: listen to a series of 3 to 7 single digit numbers, and then repeat the series; listen to a series of 4 single digit numbers, add 1 to each of the numbers, and then report the transformed series.

Kahneman and Beatty found a number of regularities in their data. In the first place, as the subject heard each digit, the pupils would get progressively larger. The process Kahneman and Beatty called "loading." Then as the subject reported each digit the pupil got progressively smaller, a process which they called "unloading." The same kind of loading and unloading was found for both the recall of the series of digits and for the number transformation task. However, because the transformation task is more difficult than the simple recall of numbers, a greater degree of dilation accompanied this effort. A similar effect was seen in the simple recall task in that as the number of digits to be recalled increased the greater was the attendant dilation. While there was not too much difference in the dilation in the 3-to-6 digit recall tasks, the series of 7 numbers was attended by a *markedly* higher degree of dilation than with any of the others. This appears to be correlated with the fact that this task requires the processing of about the maximum number of novel digits that can be handled at the same time.

The authors also found an "anticipation effect" in the pupil responses of the women. Whenever subjects knew a difficult task would be posed, their pupils would dilate slightly.

Like Heinrich, Kahneman and Beatty tested for the possibility that changes in the focusing of the eye cause the observed changes in pupil size during mental activity, especially since some of the women reported having experienced some sensation of blurring of the visual field during the difficult tasks. Looking at far objects, as mentioned earlier, causes an increase in the size of the pupil. So these authors had some of their women perform the problems while looking at a point six inches away and while looking at a point six feet away. While this change in distance caused a pupil size increase of 10 per cent, the very same effects of the mental tasks upon pupil size were observed. Hence it is absolutely clear, from our own research as earlier mentioned, from that of Heinrich, and of Kahneman and Beatty, that the pupil size changes observed during mental processes are not mediated by changes in the focusing of the eye.

Another interesting effect reported by Kahneman and Beatty was that as the subjects performed the same kind of task over and over again, the pupil response accompanying the task became somewhat smaller; thus showing that as a "response set" is acquired, the subjective difficulty of the task and the "load" are less. This is similar to Polt's findings. Kahneman and Beatty concluded that "the appearance of such practice effects in the pupillary response appears to provide additional evidence for the validity of this response as an indicator of processing load."

Another study of pupil responses in mental multiplication was carried out at the Educational Testing Service by Donald T. Payne, Mary Ellen Parry, and Stefan J. Harasymiw. They used 16 different multiplication problems to be solved mentally, and assessed them as being of four levels of difficulty according to the number of digits involved and the number of "carrying over" steps required. While the items within each level of difficulty were not presented in order of increasing difficulty, the four levels of difficulty were consecutively presented in order of increasing difficulty. Level 1 consisted of problems such as $4 \times 7$; level 2, of problems such as $74 \times 7$; level 3, of problems such as $545 \times 5$; and level 4, of problems such as $7574 \times 7$.

On the whole, pupil sizes showed progressive increases with problem difficulty. While there were several cases of reversals in pupil size between problems adjacent to each other in difficulty among the 16 problems, the Spearman rank order correlation between mean pupil size and mean difficulty, measured in terms of how long it took to solve the problems, was +.973. After they had finished solving all the problems, the subjects were also requested to indicate the order of difficulty for the problems. The mean subjective estimates of problem difficulty also correlated very highly with the mean amount of time it took to solve the problems. In this case the Spearman rank order correlation was +.991. The correlation between mean estimated problem difficulty and mean pupil dilation was +.974. The rank order correlation between the percentage of correct solutions for each problem and the mean time taken to solve them was +.924. And, finally, the rank order correlation between pupil dilation and the proportion of correct solutions was +.873. Since perfect agreement is 1.00 one can see how well these measures correlated.

The dilation figures reported by Payne, Parry, and Harasymiw are not comparable to those reported by Hess and Polt in 1964 because the measurements on which they were based were taken at different points in the pupil response protocol. For example, Hess and Polt used as control data the 2½-second period prior to the giving of the problem. For assessing the dilation effect, Hess and Polt used the 2½-second period prior to the giving of the answer. In contrast, Payne, Parry, and Harasymiw had an 8-second period between the presentation of each problem and used the pupil size during the entire period to determine the control data. This means that the recovery of the pupil size from solving the previous problem is included in these authors' control period, which would raise the control level even though the recovery is rapid. Their depiction of a typical subject's records shows a decreasing pupil size during the control period. Furthermore, the entire period during which the subject was doing her calculations formed the basis for the response data. All this, of course, would result in giving lower pupil dilation values than those given by Hess and Polt because then the control values would be higher and the response values would be lower. Hence, while the specific figures they cited for the pupil response to mental calculation are not like those of Hess and Polt, the protocol obtained from one of their subjects does resemble those of Hess and Polt. So it becomes quite clear, when all these factors are considered, that their results actually confirm the findings of all the previously published reports.

Even in New Zealand one can hear of studies conducted on the pupil response to mental calculation tasks. J. Bradshaw of the University of Otago, who carried out an investigation while he was at the University of Sheffield, confirmed that a peak in the dilation of the pupil was followed by a sharp post-solution drop when single-solution anagrams or mental arithmetic problems involving division were solved. Similarly, difficult problems resulted in an overall higher degree of dilations than the easier ones did. He also found the same phenomenon when the same kind of arithmetic material was to be answered by two different techniques, one harder than the other. The easier method was accompanied by a lower level of dilation. Bradshaw has interpreted pupillometric processing load as an index of arousal, whereas others, such as David A. Johnson, consider arousal as a factor *also* affecting pupillary phenomena.

Still further confirmation of the effects of mental activity on the size of the pupil has been provided by research conducted at Science and Engineering, Inc. by Theodore Schaefer, Jr. and his associates. Pupil diameter increased during memorization and especially during recall; item difficulty and storage load both influenced the magnitude of dilation during recall. In the first study, pupil diameter increases were found to be correlated with item difficulty, adaptation to the problem-solving situation, and novelty. In the second study, it was shown that pupil dilation served better as an indicator of memory processing load than did recall error scores. Frank Colman and Allan Paivio have similarly suggested that the latency of pupil responses may be a more sensitive peripheral response measure than GSR during cognitive tasks.

As mentioned earlier, Roubinovitch reported that pupil dilation during mental processing occurs only when subjects are actually doing mental processing, a finding we also obtained in my laboratory. That is, if a person finds a mental task very difficult or impossible he will not work on it and his pupil will not dilate. Two studies bearing upon this have been reported recently. Frederic Boersma, Keri Wilton, Richard Barham, and Walter Muir investigated the effect of column addition difficulty upon pupil size responses in normal I.Q. 11-year-old children and in educable mental retardate children who had a similar mental age but mean I.Q. of 72. Increasing the length of single-digit addition columns caused correspondingly greater pupil size during addition in normal children. This indicates that the normal children were able to accommodate and process the increased load. Their error scores rose slightly with increased difficulty, whereas the educable retardates' error scores rose sharply. The educable retardates had pupil dilation to the easiest problems, which they solved reasonably well, but only slight further increases in pupil size in response to increasing problem difficulty. Hence, they could actually process the easiest problems efficiently whereas with the harder ones, they were not able to take on the full additional mental processing load necessary to solve the problems efficiently.

The effects of lesser ability in causing subjects to expend more effort in mental processing tasks which are within the limits of the ability possessed is shown in David Crough's study of pupil response in two subject groups differing in reasoning ability. The subjects lower in reasoning ability had greater pupil dilation during reasoning tasks than did those higher in reasoning ability. The importance of individual differences in pupillometric manifestations of mental processing has also been shown by W. Scott Peavler.

Another variable affecting mental processing is motivation. For example, greater incentives for learning will not only improve learning behavior but also result in increased effort being put into learning. This is shown by the pupil size changes during high-incentive learning being larger than in low-incentive learning as reported by Daniel Kahneman and W. Scott Peavler. Other work by Kahneman and his associates suggests that the incentive effect is more likely in easier tasks than in difficult ones.

Obviously there is yet much that can be done by using the pupil response to study mental activity. The basic phenomena are extremely clear and consistent. In fact, it is easy to demonstrate it on oneself by looking into a mirror and multiplying a number such as 14 $\times$ 12. Of course, it can always be tried with acquaintances.

One interesting anecdote about our mental arithmetic research relates to a talk I gave at the American Psychological Association meetings when they convened in Los Angeles in 1964. At that time I reported the results of my study relating to the propaganda value of the various materials in relation to the Goldwater and Johnson campaign. However, in the introduction to the work I reported briefly on some of our other findings because I thought they might be interesting and stimulating to other pupil researchers. One of these pupil researchers who had read our account of this mental arithmetic process got up at the end of my talk and stated in front of several hundred people that he had tried to repeat the experiment in which individuals were asked to solve problems and, unfortunately, had not been able to duplicate the results. I asked what he meant. He said that he had gotten no increases in pupil diameter during the problem solution and no returning back to normal subsequent to this. I was dumbfounded by this report because we had for some time been using mental arithmetic as a *demonstration* device in our laboratory whenever we had visitors—either those interested in pupil research as such or just interested in some of the work going on at the University. In fact, I had set up an apparatus in conjunction with a closed-circuit television camera and receiver in such a way that eight or ten people could be in my combined laboratory-office. One person could serve as a subject and sit in the apparatus and the others could observe his pupil changes as he was asked to solve problems. They were able to then see this precise response in terms of a pupil dilation and the return to normal size when the subject gave his answer. We found this the simplest way to demonstrate the phenomenon since it was so reliable and one could not always depend on having an individual give the pupil responses in one way or another or on having very large responses in an individual when he was shown visual material. The pupil changes in mental arithmetic problems usually go above 10 per cent and often reach 20, 30, or 40 per cent increase in pupil diameter. This is very easy to see on a television monitor when the pupil is enlarged many times. In one such instance the president of IBM who was visiting the University acted as a subject. He later wrote a tongue-in-cheek letter saying that this was the last time he was going to serve as a subject for something of this sort and stick his head in an apparatus because he really didn't want anyone to find out that he couldn't easily multiply 13 by 17.

At any rate, this particular psychologist who had been doing pupil research had now told me that this phenomenon which we used as a demonstration device could not be duplicated in his own laboratory. I then asked a very simple question since we had described our procedure in great detail in the scientific publication. I asked, "Did you do it just the way we did it?" and his answer was an unequivocal "Yes." I could make no further comment and turned to other questions, but of course the damage had been done. I could see people in the audience exchange looks because this sort of situation, when one stands on the lecture platform, does not particularly inspire either self-confidence or good thoughts. I ran into this researcher sometime later and he invited me to have a drink with him, which I did. At this time, we again began talking about the problem he had in duplicating our results, and I suddenly realized what had happened. This man had used the Löwenstein apparatus and it necessitates darkness and dark adaptation on the part of the subject. This means that the pupils are at maximum dilation. Under this condition he had asked subjects to solve these problems, and unfortunately, the pupils obviously could not get much bigger as they were already at maximum dilation. It is as though you were trying to make the hole in the doughnut bigger than the doughnut itself, and this is manifestly impossible. I don't quite remember what I said, but I'm sure that all the way back to my hotel I must have been muttering to myself about the same kind of problem that has been expressed so well by James D. Watson in his book *The Double Helix*. That is, not all scientists are necessarily intelligent, inventive, or interesting.

Patrick Shrout, a student in my laboratory recently used another type of problem-solving situation in relation to pupil change. Subjects were presented with a series of statements and were asked whether they were true or false. With some of his subjects he obtained no great pupil changes for this self-assessment. In a number, however, he obtained tremendous pupil changes. They were the largest we have ever obtained. For example, to the statement "It doesn't bother me much to have someone get the best of me in a discussion," a subject's pupils dilated *115* per cent before the true or false answer was given. Other large dilation changes for subjects ranged from 50 to 118 per cent increase in pupil diameter. It was also interesting to note that some subjects apparently did not go through any extensive soul searching and had relatively small pupil changes. Perhaps this holds potential to learn something about the behavior of man.

In several experiments we noted that those individuals who were characterized by psychological tests as being introverts or extroverts also were different in their pupil responses. On the whole, those people who were categorized as introverts by the usual psychological tests had greater pupil responses than did those who were categorized as being extroverts.

The greater autonomic reactivity of introverts to sensory events has also been found by H. J. and Sybil Eysenck of Maudsley Hospital in London. Four drops of pure lemon juice caused significantly more salivation in people who were characterized as introverts than in people characterized as extroverts on the basis of a 57-item personality test. The correlation between degree of salivation and degree of introversion was approximately +.74.

Another difference we found was that those subjects who on a rating scale considered themselves to be cold, intellectual, and analytical had smaller pupil changes than those who on that same scale considered themselves to be warm, friendly, and creative individuals. The problem with all this, however, is, What does this mean? What biological use is the pupil response? There is a possibility that it may tie in with the fact that when the pupil opens there is greater light stimulation and there is more, so to speak, of the stimulus coming in to be received by the brain; and that something which is distasteful, negative, or of no particular benefit to the organism may be shut out through the lesser amount of light which is allowed to stimulate the retina of the eye.

It has amused me to think of some of the old sayings which may have something to do with pupil response. All of us know the phrase, "finally he saw the light" which means that the solution has come to the individual. It is perfectly clear that, given a normal amount of light with the pupil at a certain size for that amount of illumination, if the individual now solves a problem and the kind of response occurs which I have shown in an earlier chapter (where the pupil reaches a maximum dilation of perhaps 20–30 per cent increase of pupil diameter which is normal for that given amount of light), then obviously, the greater light input resulting from this larger pupil opening could, in fact, cause a psychologically perceivable increase in the illumination of the world as the person looks around him. It, too, might explain the interesting phenomenon of a statement such as, "when he woke up in the morning, refreshed and cheerful, the world seemed brighter," where obviously a condition of optimism, of anticipatory pleasure, ought to cause increased pupil size so that indeed, the world may psychologically look brighter. The opposite, depression or negative attitudes possibly could cause constriction and so the world, for those individuals, might be dreary from the perceptual standpoint. Obviously, this is speculation. I think, however, that this is experimentally testable and one of the projects we have on the long list of things to do involves an investigation of just these things.

# 10

# The Pupil and
# Other Measures

In an earlier chapter I discussed some of the results in which we had contradictory responses, that is, responses to pictures where we did not expect to get large pupil responses because we assumed them to be negative. For example, in those pictures which involved mutilated bodies or a concentration camp, we occasionally had large pupil responses which, according to our notion, were not realistic or expected. At least, we would not expect them if we assumed that in every case big pupils mean that the individual is responding to the stimulus in terms of a pleasant experience. We noted this very early in our experiments some years ago and thought that possibly what could be occurring was extreme arousal or, as the term is used in psychological circles, strong autonomic response.

Now there are other ways through which one can get information about such arousal. The arousal obtained is similar to that measured by the lie detector. It seemed that one of the first things to try would be to see whether or not the GSR or Galvanic Skin Response could be used in combination with the pupil. Dr. Allan Rechtschaffen, whom we mentioned earlier, allowed us to move our equipment to his sleep and dream laboratory. We had a number of subjects who were completely wired for the sort of experiments he was carrying out. We not only had the Galvanic Skin Response which could be monitored in another room but also information on heart rate and the alpha rhythm as shown by an electroencephalogram.

Now let us discuss these one by one. The Galvanic Skin Response is really a measure of changes in the electrical conductivity of the skin surface. These electrical conductivity changes are due to changes in skin sweating rate, which is in turn influenced by autonomic nervous system activity changes. Therefore the GSR is used by some researchers to indicate the nature of moment-to-moment changes in the activity of the autonomic nervous system.

You may notice that under some conditions of anxiety your palms begin to sweat. This causes a lowering in the conductance of the electrical circuit used in the GSR equipment and shows as a marked response on the pen and ink recorder which continually monitors the skin conductivity. If the Galvanic Skin Response equipment is working while the subject is relaxed and no activity is going on, a relatively smooth line is recorded. The instant that the person is shown, say, a shocking picture, there would be a deflection of the pen indicating a change in the conductivity. This response is relatively rapid. It takes place within a second or so of the onset of the stimulation.

Heart rate is, of course, obvious enough. One would expect an increase in heart rate until, as everyone knows, under certain kinds of arousal conditions the heart begins to pound and increases in frequency by as much as 50 per cent or more. The same increase in heart rate, of course, can result because of an increased work effort. Just jumping up and down ten times will cause a marked increase in heart rate.

The alpha rhythm of the brain waves is somewhat different. This is taken from an electrode fastened to the back of the head (an area called the occipital lobe). Under conditions of quiet, particularly when the eyes are closed, this alpha rhythm is most individuals consists of about eight or ten waves per second. When the person orients or thinks of a problem this alpha rhythm ceases and instead we have a "hash" or random waviness which is recorded on the equipment. We recorded all of these measures simultaneously with the pupil response while showing one of our standard series of pictures which included those which we reported in an earlier chapter dealing with our first experiment. We also added five more which consisted of what we called at that time "horror pictures": a mutilated body, a concentration camp, and so on, as well as two additional, more neutral pictures involving landscapes.

The results were quite interesting. In the case of one of our women subjects, the highest pupil response actually was for the nude pinup. Next highest was the picture of the mutilated body; then came the response to the nude man and the others followed with the lowest responses to the landscapes. When we looked at the other physiological measures, however, we found a very interesting difference. Here the greatest GSR deflection given by the subject was to the mutilated body, next to the picture of the female pinup, while the responses to the nude male were scarcely noticeable. There were no deflections on the GSR record for such pictures as the landscape or the mother and child, in spite of the fact that the mother and child produced a reasonably good pupil increase.

In the case of heart rate, we found that it increased for the picture of the mutilated body and for the male pinup but we could find no significant changes in heart rate for the other pictures. The alpha rhythm again showed a loss for most of the pictures but by the time we got to the second and third landscape the alpha rhythm had returned. One could therefore say that the amount of arousal as far as it was measured by the alpha rhythm was negligible for these particular photographs.

Now what does all this mean? Looking at the data, which included similar responses from other people, it seemed quite clear to me that what we had was a situation in which arousal itself, as measured by other physiological means was giving us information that greatly added to the possible interpretation of the pupil data. Let us take, for example, just the three photographs to which the subjects had a high pupil response: the female pinup, the horror picture, and the nude male. All of these had high pupil responses and one might ordinarily say that these were all positive or pleasant pictures as far as the subject was concerned. But remember, as far as the Galvanic Skin Response and the increase in heart rate were concerned, this occurred only to the photographs of the horror picture and the female nude.

Now one could easily say that the nude female and the horror picture caused a considerable amount of arousal and this arousal, of course, need not be positive. It can be arousal in a negative sense. It can come from disgust, horror, shock, embarrassment, or a number of other essentially negative responses. So we could rank the pictures, as far as the pupil is concerned, on an arbitrary scale and say the highest response is to the picture of the female nude and close behind it, the picture of the mutilated body, and third the male pinup. But we would have to say that the pupils really were not as big as they ought to be for the kind of response that we were getting as indicated by the strong emotional arousal which we measured by the GSR or by the heart rate. In both instances we know that the pupil will be driven to a larger size by anything which involves emotional arousal, whether good or bad. We can see that it is possible to subtract the effect of emotional arousal which would account for a certain amount of pupil dilation and then we can see what is left. This will give us the positive, or in some instances, the negative response as the pupil indicates it. This would have to be in accord with the logarithmic effect of pupil response, an effect which will be discussed later.

Let us take an even simpler example and make one fundamental assumption. Unfortunately, this assumption is not as yet based on reliable data, but we are now working on the problem and I think that there is every hope that we will be able to have an answer in the next year or two. This assumption is that we can measure and quantify, in terms of a scale, the response strength both for the pupil and for the Galvanic Skin Response. We will talk about it in terms of percentages of a total possible response. In other words, let us suppose the total possible response for the pupil would be a 100 per cent increase in pupil diameter—that is, for example, from $4\frac{1}{2}$ to 9 millimeters. We will similarly suppose that we can detect a 100 per cent increase in the Galvanic Skin Response and see how much of a percentage compared to that possible total of 100 per cent we are getting. A 100 per cent response might occur both for the pupil and for the GSR if the subject is unexpectedly subjected to pain. In that moment, we would expect to get maximum pupil dilation and a maximum GSR response.

Now let us look at two pictures. One is the female nude and the other one is the male nude. To the female nude we get a 20 per cent increase in pupil diameter; to the male nude we get an 18 per cent increase in pupil diameter. These two responses are not significantly different from each other. However, when we now look at the arousal which these two photographs produce in our subjects we find that we get a 30 per cent increase in the Galvanic Skin Response for the female nude and only a 5 per cent increase in the Galvanic Skin Response for the picture of the nude man. Subtracting in each case because we know that the arousal as measured by the GSR actually produces a certain amount of pupil dilation, we come out with a very simple answer; that is, a minus 10 per cent or a 10 per cent *constriction* of the pupil because the pupil is not as big as it should have been for the amount of autonomic arousal produced by the picture of the female nude. In the case of the picture of the male pinup we end up with a 13 per cent increase—a positive response as far as the pupil is concerned—because by subtracting the small deflection of the GSR we still have a 13 per cent pupil dilation remaining. We can therefore say that the picture of the male nude is interesting or attractive to this female subject.

Use of this sort of manipulation is admittedly arbitrary except for the fact that it can be done equally for all stimuli. We find very quickly that in many instances what look like abnormal responses actually turn out to be quite normal and all is right again with the world since *most* of our subjects thus show larger responses to what we might consider the appropriate visual stimulus. Again, of course, we hope that it will be possible to refine this subtracting method by taking into account the logarithmic effect of pupil response (which will be described in a later section). We can obtain quite the same thing with our horror pictures. For the picture of a mutilated body we may get a higher response than we get for the male nude, but we also get a very high GSR and, by a similar computation, find very quickly that actually we are getting a response which is nowhere as big as it should be for the amount of GSR arousal. Therefore, we can consider the response actually to be negative. In the cases where we do not get a GSR or an increase in heart rate we can take the pupil response at its face value and use the small increases or decreases or sometimes even greater decreases if we are dealing with mildly distasteful stimuli such as the picture of the cross-eyed boy, and do not have to subtract from this the response that is indicated by the GSR. We have had quite a few of this sort of stimuli which do not give a GSR deflection but actually give a pupil constriction. I have already mentioned some of these pictures, and to this list we might add the picture of an atrociously decorated interior or a photograph of an abstract painting that makes no sense to the individual even though he may say he likes modern art. All these can give considerable pupil constrictions without any other apparent, at least to us, physiological change that could be considered part of an arousal pattern. We have carried out experiments over the last six years in which we have periodically gathered information on the Galvanic Skin Response or changes in heart rate and sometimes a combination of both. It has helped us gain insights about the way in which people respond. The difficulty is that not all people tested show clear GSR's. Therefore, the GSR is not as universal as the pupil response because everyone we have ever tested has shown pupil responses. One exception does come to mind. In one of the records obtained at Marplan (a market research group) no change was detected in the pupil. It turned out that the person's left eye was *glass.*

It is also interesting that in solving simple mental arithmetic problems, the heart rate goes up, the Galvanic Skin Response usually shows a deflection, and the alpha rhythm of the EEG drops out. Some of this—for example, the latter—was reported earlier in this decade and the GSR and heart rate changes in relation to problem-solving have been long known. There is one important point to remember, however, and that is that in all these cases there seems to be no differentiation on the part of these stimuli between positive and negative responses. In other words, you get a GSR increase in all instances whether the picture shown is positive to a great degree or negative to a great degree, and it would therefore be impossible to tell the difference between the Galvanic Skin Responses in such cases. For example, let us take three cases: we get a high GSR response to the picture of the nude female, we get a 5 per cent GSR deflection to the picture of the naked male, and we get a zero GSR response to the picture of the landscape. How, then, can we evaluate the meaning of these three pictures? One possibility is to say that the first is the most arousing, the second less, and, of course, the third not at all. However, if we take the pupil response in conjunction with the GSR we come to a much more sensible ranking of the stimulus value of these three pictures, as indicated before. This ranking would be as follows: (1) male, positive; (2) landscape, neutral; and (3) nude female, negative.

In the light of these considerations I have concluded that pupillometrics, to be maximally useful, should be combined with as much other nonverbal information as possible, such as simultaneous GSR, EKG, EMG (electromyograph), and EEG. I do not believe that behavior can be adequately measured or understood by the use of only one yardstick. All these measures tap in on different aspects of the same behaving organism. Certainly it may be found that in some cases one measure may be more useful than another.

One of my former students, Dr. Niles Bernick, in collaboration with Dr. Gene Borowitz and Dr. Arthur Kling of the Department of Psychiatry of the University of Illinois College of Medicine, has reported on a study which I would like to discuss in detail because it covers an area which we have not directly investigated in our own experimental work. These workers were interested in the effect of sexual arousal and sexual anxiety as it might relate to pupil size and, in conjunction with it, used two physiological measures which normally go along with changes in autonomic activity. In this way, they hoped to be able to measure the concurrent effects of two strong emotional states, sexual arousal and anxiety, in response to stimuli which were essentially harmless or innocuous. The pupil response was measured in an apparatus which was like the one which I described earlier since Dr. Bernick helped in the development of that apparatus while he was a student and my assistant. Heart rate was measured as another indicator because it has long been considered a general index of activation or arousal and this was monitored during the testing session. In addition, the blood steroid count was taken. This, explained as simply as possible, refers to the level of plasma 17-hydroxycorticosteroids in the blood of the subject. This has been found by other workers to provide a physiological index of anxiety since it is known that in subjective states of fear, anger, and anxiety, the level of this plasma steroid increases. The subjects used were eight graduate or medical student volunteers between the ages of 22 and 30, all of whom had given a history of heterosexual interest and experience. As stated before, the pupil diameter was obtained by the usual method, using our apparatus, while an electrocardiogram continually recorded the heart rate.

As for the steroid level, three blood samples of 10 cubic centimeters each were drawn from a vein at different times. The first sample was drawn at 2:00 in the afternoon when the subject entered the laboratory. The second sample was drawn between 2:45 and 3:00 P.M., near the end of the experiment, and the third sample was obtained one hour later. This blood was then appropriately treated in order to determine the steroid level.

The actual material which was shown consisted of 2 × 2 slides and three movies. All of them were in black and white. The slide set was made up of 12 photographs, 6 of women and 6 of men, in each case preceded by a gray field control. In this case, rather than using the numbers which we have on our control slides, each one of the slides had a central fixation point at which the subject could look. The photographs themselves were nonprovocative clippings from popular magazines. These slides had been used previously in a developmental study of children's pupil responses. We will say something more about that particular study in a later chapter. Each photograph was presented, as is the case in our experiments, for a ten-second period so that it took a total of four minutes for the whole set.

One of three movies was shown in an experimental session. Movie A was an erotic "stag movie" which included a range of heterosexual activity. Movie B was a suspense film produced by Alfred Hitchcock for television, and Movie C was an erotic homosexual movie which showed two males in a variety of homosexual activities. Proper safeguards were taken to keep the brightness level relatively constant throughout the total exposure of slides and motion picture films. Movie A was presented in the first experimental session, Movie B was presented two to four weeks later, and Movie C followed another two to six weeks later.

The experimental procedure for each of the subjects in each of the three sessions was as follows: (1) diagnostic interview one to three weeks prior to first experimental day; (2) blood sample no. 1 drawn for corticosteroids at 2:00 P.M.; (3) (a) light adaptation in the pupillometer for a period of 1 minute and 40 seconds, (b) slides of clothed males and females, 4 minutes, (c) movie, 16 minutes; (4) interview, 10 minutes; (5) blood sample no. 2 at 2:45 to 3:00 P.M.; (6) (a) light adaptation in pupillometer, 1 minute 40 seconds, (b) slides of clothed males and females repeated, 4 minutes; (7) blood sample no. 3 at 3:45 to 4:00 P.M. In the 10 minute interview which followed the showing of the movie the subjects were asked to evaluate the arousal caused by the movie in terms of reported erection. A summary of the findings is as follows. The verbal report of which movie caused the greatest sexual arousal or whether or not the subject had a greater or lesser amount of arousal agreed with the pupil size changes. It did not matter whether the subject was aroused by the stag movie or by the homosexual movie. In other words, there was agreement that the larger the amount of erection produced by the movie the greater was the pupil diameter increase. However, increased steroid levels, which might be considered to indicate increased anxiety, were not particularly observed in those individuals who reported to be aroused by the stag movie. On the other hand, some individuals who reported being sexually aroused and also had increased steroid levels at the same time the arousal was elicited were stimulated as the result of seeing the homosexual movie. This finding can certainly be easily interpreted in terms of a general arousal in response to the homosexual movie. It is in this regard quite similar to what I have previously discussed wherein anxiety might also be recorded by a measure such as the GSR. In this case we would expect the pupil to show the effect of interest and also to reflect the amount of upheaval in the autonomic nervous system which accompanies the showing of the homosexual movie.

Further, there was an increase in the heart rate in the subjects who were stimulated by the stag movie. However, the amount of acceleration was negatively correlated with the degree of reported sexual arousal; that is, the more aroused subjects, in terms of their report of erection, showed the smallest increase in heart rate. Again, if we remember that the verbal report of sexual arousal was highly correlated with the pupil size, this leads us to a situation in which the greater positive response makes sense in terms of those individuals who were highly positively stimulated by the stag movie but did not necessarily have the increased pupil dilation which might go along with an increase in heart rate. These findings were relatively clear. In addition, there were two findings which, while not having any high degree of statistical significance, did suggest that the subjects aroused by the stag movie tended to have increased pupil responses later in the test session even when viewing innocuous photographs of women.

Those subjects who were aroused by the homosexual film tended to show an increased pupil size when viewing innocuous photographs of male subjects. We have explored similar possibilities in relation to the homosexual study previously reported in this book. It could well be that with this sort of experimental procedure, using the pupil response and some concurrent physiological index, it will be possible to explore latent homosexuality which is of considerable importance in psychiatric circles. It may be that in spite of the fact that the individuals who were used in the test by Bernick and his associates were to all intents and purposes practicing heterosexuals, a latent homosexuality existed in some of them. The last finding was that three subjects showed or reported rather high levels of arousal to both of the erotic movies. This suggests then that in some individuals sexual arousal may be nonspecific to the contents of the stimulus but rather relates to any general sexual situation.

This, then, gives a clear indication that the pupil response in combination with other physiological measures can be a powerful tool in discriminating attitudes which may be relatively hidden even to the consciousness of the individual concerned. There are obviously a great many other possible ways to use this response. Some of our previous research material clearly seems to indicate if one can assume good faith on the part of the experimental subjects, that they may have definite negative feelings or positive feelings about things and yet sincerely profess quite the opposite. In this regard let us now consider such possibilities in the next chapter where we will deal with the effects of pupil research on advertising and marketing.

# 11

# Advertising and the Pupil

From 1951 to 1958 I had some brief contacts with the advertising and marketing world as a consultant to help in the design of some perceptual research studies. For example, sometime in the 1950s I designed a study to see whether or not better quality or greater fidelity of sound on a television set would in any way give the viewer the impression that the picture was better or had greater fidelity. This was done very simply by showing subjects a taped television program shown on the same monitor but which in one session had very poor quality sound, using the normally inexpensive speaker with which most television sets come equipped, and in one session using the very best sound that could be built into a television. This would cost extra money to produce, of course. The results did indicate a small increase in the apparent superiority of the TV picture when the sound was better, but the difference was not of sufficient value to justify the greater expenditure of money involved in making better sound equipment which would then make the price of the television set noncompetitive in the field.

With some of this background it was not entirely unusual that I was asked, in the latter part of 1959, to help in setting up a perception laboratory for Interpublic, the second largest advertising and marketing organization in the United States. I did not agree to this without some soul searching. There is a peculiar problem when a psychologist in the academic community has contact with Madison Avenue. Colleagues take a dim view. I have often tried to fathom this behavior on the part of the other academicians and have come to the conclusion that working for the advertising firms is usually associated with making a great amount of additional money. Perhaps academicians, being only human, are subject to a certain amount of envy due to such an impression. At any rate, there is no question in the minds of most academicians that they "know" that they too, if only they were willing to prostitute themselves, could obtain a great deal of money from the advertising world or some other industrial organization. What most of them don't realize is that they have neither the capacity, nor the imagination, nor the kind of drive that is necessary to have profit-making businesses pay good money for their services. These organizations will not pay for diffident, incompetent, and nit-picking contributions.

In fact, the academician is in some respects a most unusual animal. Although he seems to abhor the earning of additional funds by some sort of association with industry or advertising, he is easily able to rationalize benefits which accrue to him. There are many examples of this. One instance involves expense-paid travel to interesting places.

It would not ordinarily occur to an academic group to have a conference or a meeting in a place like New York, Washington or Chicago, if it can possibly be avoided. Not too many years ago a group of advisers to one of our federal research granting agencies decided that they would have to find out something about the European ethological movement that has been taking place. Ethologists are people with a different approach to the problems of behavior, placing much more emphasis on total behavior patterns involving the environment rather than the isolated nerve reflex and muscle movements which are studied so often in the laboratory. A large number of ethologists come from three countries: Germany, Holland and England. There are a few additional ones in France, Switzerland and the Scandinavian countries. I therefore assumed that probably this group in the United States would decide to go to one of the more interesting places and I made a mental bet that it would be Paris or Copenhagen or maybe even London. But it turned out that I was completely wrong. Rome was obviously the "right place" and that's where the meeting was held. I feel no great objection to this. I think it is good that professors have an opportunity to get away for a period each year from their routine of work and teaching. I mention it only because of the horror-stricken faces I have seen when it is found out that someone has been doing something which pays some money—work that allows him to take a trip to a domestic or international conference at his personal expense rather than using money which could be utilized to carry out research.

At any rate, my primary task for Interpublic, which began in the fall of 1959, consisted of setting up a perception laboratory in which the organization might carry out basic research which might conceivably have some ultimate benefits for the corporation. The laboratory did not need to show any tangible, practical results for a year or so. I thought this was a good challenge and an interesting problem, and agreed to take on the consultant-directorship of Interpublic's perception laboratory. The idea was that all the research equipment and procedures would be installed in about six months and that this would be the total of my commitment to that organization. The rooms to be used for the perception research laboratory had already been established and, in fact, an assistant had already been hired.

I went to New York to discuss the possibilities of my undertaking the assignment with Marion Harper, Jr. I had heard of Mr. Harper and his one-man rule of Interpublic, which is a vast empire of advertising, public relations, marketing, and other communications companies. At our first meeting I noticed a very unusual thing. I was not particularly apprehensive about the meeting. I looked forward to it with some enthusiasm because I had heard that Mr. Harper was receptive to original ideas and I thought I had some new angles on how a perception laboratory could be set up without the necessity of too much verbal questionnaire type research. I got to this type of procedure quite naturally from my work with animals because obviously you cannot ask an animal what it sees or what something means to it. Hence one must devise test techniques which get at preferences and perceptions without the necessity of questionnaires. Just before we were to meet Harper I noticed that the two gentlemen who accompanied me, and who held high positions in the organization became extremely apprehensive. By the time we got to see Harper I began to wonder whether some of this apprehensiveness was not also rubbing off on me. However, it was extremely reassuring to talk with Harper. He was direct, asked good questions, seemed to be satisfied with my answers, and we there and then settled the question of my accepting this responsibility.

Paula Drillman was to be my assistant in the perception research laboratory. After the initial encounter of sizing up one another, we got along well and began the process of working out some perceptual techniques that I had already used with animals and humans. In a few months we had a small but, I felt, interesting and unusual perception operation going. Then early in 1960 came the day which I described previously when I sat in bed and my wife noticed my dilated pupils. I talked about this result to Paula Drillman on one of my monthly visits to New York and she also could see the obvious implications for advertising and marketing research.

In a very short time we produced a pupil apparatus which was moved to the New York perception laboratory and Paula Drillman and I began a series of what might be called basic research studies, including the kinds of material we had used in Chicago. Shortly thereafter we used pictures of packages and advertising material for the first time. The results were extremely good and at the same time extremely meaningless. The reason was simply that there was nothing with which to compare our results. In a very naïve way I had asked one of the higher-ups in the organization if they couldn't supply me with five good ads and five bad ads. I presumed that I could test these to see whether or not one could get differences in pupil responses from subjects and then hopefully be able to get a difference in line with the established good and bad ads. Unfortunately, this request simply could not be met. In fact, I learned that there just was no effective means of determining whether or not an ad really did the job that it was supposed to do. The problems related to it were much too complex and certainly it was impossible to know ahead of time whether or not an ad was potentially successful.

Slowly, until the end of my affiliation with this organization in 1967, I began to learn a lot about the advertising and marketing world but mostly I tried not to expose myself to too much information. I thought that I would be best off knowing as little as possible and attacking the problem from the standpoint of it being a scientific project where I would be able to use my own approach to try to get at the basic problem of advertising effectiveness and the prediction of marketing success.

We had already tested a number of advertising materials such as ads in magazines and different packages and package designs, when it occurred to me that one thing we might do would be to test a product or a line of products where we would subsequently be able to get information as to how well it did in the market place. One of the clients was a watch manufacturer and it was possible for us to get a series of watches of the same price, photograph them for test slides, expose them to a number of subjects, and then rank them in order of apparent appeal. My notion was that those watches which might have the greater appeal as evidenced by the pupil response would then presumably be most apt to be chosen in the jewelry store where they were displayed and sold. The results were good. The agreement between the ranked pupil responses and the actual ranks of sales figures which we were subsequently able to get was almost perfect.

Encouraged by the watch study, we carried out another one and found that while there was general agreement between the results of our study and the actual sales figures, there was one major discrepancy. This bothered me until I found a possible answer. Although the retail prices of these watches were all the same, they did not necessarily carry the same wholesale price. We discovered that in the case of our one discrepancy, a watch of a certain design series which got the greatest pupil response had the smallest amount of profit for the retailer. The actual sales figures showed a reversal between the pupil results and the sales figures. Although it is not possible to document the accuracy of my assessment, it seems perfectly appropriate to assume that the retailer will have a greater desire to sell or push the watch on which he makes the greater margin of profit. Thus, the experimental pupil situation is not a fair representation of what is being studied. It is, however, a very good example of how difficult it is by *any* research technique to predict what people will do when all the imponderables are not, and cannot be, taken fully into account. We will have more to say about these possibilities later on.

Although my original association with Interpublic was planned to last six months, it lasted seven years. Sometime after the beginning of my association with Interpublic, the organization hired the consumer psychologist Dr. Herbert Krugman, and he was involved for some years in the perception laboratory operation before joining General Electric. He published several studies in relation to the response to greeting cards and silverware, and I want to describe the results of these experiments in greater detail.

The first study involved a comparison of ten humorous greeting cards. Four of them were friendship cards and the remaining six were birthday cards. Twenty-three men and 26 women were recruited from shoppers passing by a shopping center where the pupil apparatus had been set up in a rented store. The slides of the greeting cards, alternated with the proper control slides were shown to the people individually. After seeing the slides the subjects were asked to recall what cards they had seen and then to indicate which cards in the friendship and birthday groups they liked the best and which they liked the least.

The pupil responses and the verbally given information were compared with the actual sales figures for these cards as provided by the manufacturer. Table 11 shows the results. There was a positive correlation of about +.40 within both sets of cards between sales reports and the pupil response. However, the verbally reported preferences for the birthday cards were correlated *negatively* with the pupil response to them, on the order of −.60. Furthermore, the verbally stated preference ranks for the birthday cards had a correlation of +.09 with the sales figures, which indicates a rather complete lack of any relationship between the two measures. The correlation between verbal response and sales for the friendship cards was much better, +.40.

The second study involved a series of ten different sterling silver patterns. Slides were made of each pattern shown as a single place setting consisting of a knife, fork, and spoon. The pupil apparatus was set up in an unobtrusive alcove at Georg Jensen's in New York City, and 39 women shoppers who were found examining sterling silver patterns were asked to be subjects.

First the individual subjects were shown the ten silver patterns alternated with the appropriate control slides. Then each subject was shown the actual place settings and asked to rank them in order of preference from high (1) to low (10). They were also

Table 11    Comparison of Sales, Pupil Responses, and Verbal Ratings for Greeting Cards

| Title of card | Sales Rank | Pupil Response | | Verbal Rank |
| | | Rank | Per Cent Change | |
|---|---|---|---|---|
| (Friendship)[a] | | | | |
| Hi! | 1 | 3 | − .1 | 2 |
| Awkward Age | 2 | 1 | +1.7 | 3 |
| Dolce Vita | 3 | 2 | +1 | 1 |
| You're Nice | 4 | 4 | − .2 | 4 |
| (Birthday)[b] | | | | |
| Old as Hills | 1 | 1 | +2.9 | 4 |
| Elephant | 2 | 6 | − .1 | 2 |
| Swiss Cheese | 3 | 2 | +2.7 | 5 |
| Cane | 4 | 4 | +1.7 | 1 |
| Witch | 5 | 3 | +1.8 | 6 |
| Horn | 6 | 5 | + .4 | 3 |

[a]Rank order coefficient:  Sales rank with pupil rank = +.4
                Sales rank with verbal rank = +.4
                Neither value is significant.
[b]Rank order coefficient:  Sales rank with pupil rank = +.37
                Sales rank with verbal rank = +.09
                Neither value is significant.
Reprinted from Krugman, H. *Journal of Marketing Research,* **1,** 15–19 (November, 1964), published by the American Marketing Association.

asked whether they had actually been shopping for silver patterns, or were just browsing. Thirteen of these subjects turned out to be actual shoppers. Interestingly enough they had greater overall pupil responses to the picture slides than the browsers did.

Since these ten sterling patterns were an exclusive line identified with the store, the management was able to provide their sales history. Table 12 shows the sales ranks, pupil ranks, and verbally reported ranks for each of the ten patterns, with the shoppers and the browsers treated as separate categories.

The data of this table in conjunction with the remarks of the

**Table 12   Comparison of Sales, Pupil Responses and Verbal Ratings for Silverware**

| | | Shoppers[b] | | | Browsers | | |
|---|---|---|---|---|---|---|---|
| Pattern[c] | Sales[a] Rank | Pupil Rank | Per Cent Change | Verbal Rank | Pupil Rank | Per Cent Change | Verbal Rank |
| Acorn | 1 | 5 | + .5 | 8 | 1 | +1 | 2 |
| Acanthus | 2 | 1 | +2.3 | 6.5 | 3 | + .2 | 4.5 |
| Cactus | 3 | 7 | − .9 | 3 | 6 | − .1 | 3 |
| Cypress | 4 | 3 | +1.7 | 4 | 5 | .0 | 7 |
| Continental | 5 | 2 | +2.1 | 2 | 2 | + .6 | 4.5 |
| Pyramid | 6 | 10 | −2.6 | 1 | 8 | −1.4 | 1 |
| Blossom | 7 | 9 | −2.2 | 10 | 10 | −3.7 | 10 |
| Caravel | 8 | 4 | + .8 | 9 | 4 | + .1 | 9 |
| Argo | 9.5 | 6 | − .1 | 6.5 | 7 | − .9 | 8 |
| Nordic | 9.5 | 8 | −1.4 | 5 | 9 | −2.2 | 6 |

[a]The following rank-order correlations were obtained:
   Sales rank with shoppers' pupil rank = +.43
   Sales rank with shoppers' verbal rank = +.14
   Sales rank with browsers' pupil rank = +.66 ($p = .05$)
   Sales rank with browsers' verbal rank = +.60 ($p = .05$)
[b]The shoppers' per cent change in pupil dilation was more favorable than the browsers', i.e., larger plus per cent or smaller minus per cent, for seven of the ten patterns, suggesting greater interest in silverware in general on the part of the shoppers. A one-trial test of this hypothesis shows that $t = 1.84$, $df = 9$, $p = .05$.
[c]Retailer's comments:
   Acorn        "This gets the bulk of our advertising by far"
   Acanthus
   Cactus
   Cypress      "Sells better out of town"
   Continental  "Only pattern that doubled its volume in recent years—will be advertised next year"
   Pyramid      "What the public thinks is tasteful but isn't"
   Blossom
   Caravel      "A 'designer's design'—not expected to sell in the USA"
   Argo         "Introduced in 1963 and not doing well"
   Nordic       "Discontinued years ago—didn't sell"
Reprinted from Krugman, H. *Journal of Marketing Research*, **1**, 15–19 (November, 1964), published by the American Marketing Association.

retailer regarding several of the patterns give some very interesting facts. For example, for the "Pyramid" design, the retailer remarked that it was a pattern that the public thought was tasteful but which really wasn't. This received the top *verbal* ranking from both the shoppers and the browsers but received rather low *pupil* responses from both groups. It got the smallest pupil response from the shoppers and was eighth in pupil size rank for the browsers. It was, however, in sixth place in the sales rank. This is completely congruent with the fact that people often buy things they think they like but don't really like. In many of these cases the buyer discovers, after he has had the item in his possession, that he is not really happy with it. "Acorn" was highest in sales rank and the retailer reported having advertised it the most. The browsers' pupil response ranked it first, and their verbal rank placed it second. The shoppers' pupil response put it in fifth place and their verbal responses placed it in eighth place. "Continental" placed second for both shoppers' and browsers' pupil responses, and in mid-range in the verbal responses. It was the second-place seller and the retailer noted that it was the only pattern in this set in recent years that had doubled its sales and that its advertising would be increased the next year. "Caravel," however, while ranked in ninth place in both verbal rankings was in fourth place in both pupil response rankings. It was eighth in sales, and the retailer remarked that it was a "designer's design" and was not expected to sell in this country.

Although the shoppers had larger pupil sizes to seven of the ten patterns than the browsers, thus indicating a greater interest in silverware designs, neither their pupil responses nor their verbal responses correlated as highly with actual sales rank as did the corresponding ranks for the browsers. The shoppers' pupil rank correlated $+.43$ with sales, and their verbal rank correlated only $+.14$ with sales. With the browsers, however, the pupil rank correlated $+.66$ with sales, and the verbal ranking correlated $+.60$ with sales. Both of these correlations were statistically significant.

These results with silverware patterns clearly demonstrate that "the impact of the environment is often difficult to determine from conscious impressions that are verbally reported," as Krugman stated. People may not be able to report their feelings accurately in certain areas where there are cultural, social, or "prestige" factors exerting pressures for people to react in certain ways in certain situations. Furthermore, this technique permits the circumvention of any language or translation problems in surveys of opinions in cross-cultural situations.

By far the most interesting example of our pupil study in relation to the "real" world came when we had the opportunity to pretest *Encyclopaedia Britannica* advertising before it was actually released. The work was done over a three-year period in collaboration with F. J. van Bortel, who headed the marketing section of Chicago's branch of Interpublic. This was an unusual opportunity because we were able to test different pairs of ads, each of which would be published later in a large circulation magazine in what is called a split run. This means that every other copy of the magazine has a different ad. Ad A will appear in the first copy, ad B in the second copy, ad A in the third copy, and so on, so in a completely random way as it goes out to subscribers or is picked up on a newsstand, people will be exposed equally, that is, in actual numbers, to ad A, while another group will be exposed to ad B. Factors such as seasonal fluctuation or differences between publications will not bias the results toward one ad or the other. There is a good final measure as to how effective the ad is in producing results. The people fill out a small post card which is part of the ad and send it back to the *Encyclopaedia Britannica*. The post cards are keyed so that it is known which advertisement it was in response to. This technique thus provides an accurate and objective measure of the ads' performance. We therefore have an interesting situation in that we have preliminary pupil data which, let us say, suggests that ad A gives greater pupil response than ad B. If we make the assumption that ad A therefore is more appealing and interesting than ad B, it should cause more people to be sufficiently interested to read the ad, fill out the coupon requesting further information, and then send it to *Encyclopaedia Britannica*. We would make this prediction and then some months later we would be able to find out whether or not our prediction had met with success. I might say that predictions on a purely verbal level and based on the judgment of so-called experts in the advertising firm itself often turned out to be completely wrong while the actual results, in all but one instance, of the predictions based on pupil response clearly differentiated the "winner" of the two ads. These results are highly significant. It is this sort of experimental procedure which is obviously most appealing to me because it allows a tangible result which can either prove or disprove the prediction made on the basis of the pupil response. The experiment which we did in conjunction with van Bortel went as follows.

In this series of studies the people tested for their pupil response to the ads were all "qualified prospects." This means that they had the same characteristics as do families that are the best prospects for the purchase of an encyclopedia. This was done because preliminary investigation had shown that families qualifying as prospects had larger pupil response scores to encyclopedia ads than those not qualifying as prospects—just as in the earlier silverware study the women who were actually shopping for silverware patterns had greater pupil responses to pictures of the patterns than did those who were browsers. This kind of effect has been found consistently for other products and services, and seems to me to have as yet unexploited potential.

Although the pupil measurement becomes quite stable when 30 subjects are used, 50 subjects was the minimum number used in any of the *Encyclopaedia Britannica* ad studies.

The basic technique for each study involved first showing the individual subject the slide-projected pictures of the ads in the pupil apparatus. Since encyclopedia ads normally have an appreciable amount of reading material in them, it is not possible for subjects to be able to read them in their entirety during the ten-second exposure. Hence this exposure would serve to measure the initial impact of the material, that is, the extent to which the advertisement is able to command the attention of the reader through the picture, headline, and other principal visual elements.

The next step was to place the subject in a situation in which he could read the advertisements in their entirety as he wished. He was encouraged to read the ads, but was not forced. The final step was to again show the subject the slides of the ads in the pupil apparatus as before. Thus it was possible to measure the effect of the copy itself in the responsiveness to the ad as a whole. This, then, also provides a measure of the persuasiveness of the copy, in terms of the attitude shown by the pupil response on re-exposure.

The first study, conducted in 1963, compared an ad called

"Family Telescope" with a new ad called "Boys in Pool." The "Family Telescope" ad was one that had been proven effective in getting post cards returned. The new ad had a format that was very different from that previously used by this company. Verbal questionnaire techniques had obtained a high response for this new ad. The pupil response scores for this test are shown in Table 13.

**Table 13   Pupil Responses and Card Return to Two Split-run Encyclopedia Ads**

| | Pupil-Response Scores | | | |
| | Initial Impact | Post-Readership | Total | Lead Performance |
| --- | --- | --- | --- | --- |
| Control<br>Family Telescope<br>Red books | 28 | 16 | 44 | 100% |
| Test<br>Boys in Pool | −2 | −1 | −3 | 82% |

Tables 13, 14, 15, 16, 17, 18 and 19 reprinted from Bortel, F. J. van. Commercial applications of pupillometrics. In: F. M. Bass, C. W. King and E. A. Pessemier (Eds.), *Applications of the Sciences in Marketing Management*, pp. 439–453. New York: Wiley, 1968.

Although the new ad had been rated highly by the questionnaires, the pupil response scores for it were much lower than for the old ad. Then the post card return data came to confirm this result, for it was found to return only 82 per cent as many post cards as the old one. It should be noted that differences of 10 per cent or more between ads that are being compared for post card return performance are considered significant.

In a second test the same control ad, "Family Telescope," was used in comparison with another version of the same ad which differed from the original only in that the color of the bindings of the encyclopedia set displayed in the original was red and in the modified version it was white.

Table 14 shows the pupil and post card return data for the two ads. While the pupil response for the white binding ad was greater than for the red binding ad, the difference was not significant. However, the post card returns for the white binding ad not only were greater than those for the original red binding ad but were superior to a statistically significant extent.

For the remaining studies in this series the control slides were made so as to more nearly approximate the brightness value of the picture slides. Previously, they had been slightly brighter than the controls, a factor which would tend to decrease the magnitude of the difference between the pupil responses to the control and picture slides.

**Table 14    Pupil Responses and Card Return to Two Split-run Encyclopedia Ads**

| | Pupil-Response Scores | | | |
| | Initial Impact | Post-Readership | Total | Lead Performance |
| --- | --- | --- | --- | --- |
| Control<br>Family Telescope<br>Red books | 28 | 16 | 44 | 100% |
| Test<br>Family Telescope<br>White books | 34 | 37 | 71 | 110% |

In the next study the control ad was similar to the one used in the first two studies and, like that ad, had a red binding on the encyclopedia set it displayed. It was called "Boy and Girl." It was compared with a new ad called "Knowledge." As Table 15 shows, the old ad had a slightly higher initial impact than the new ad. However, the post-readership scores were no different, which corresponded perfectly with the practically equal performance in returned post cards.

It was then decided to test this old ad with a version that had a white binding on the encyclopedia set it displayed, since in the earlier study the identical ad differing only in the color of the book bindings showed a greater response for the white binding over the red. Table 16 shows that the very same results were obtained with the red and white binding versions of the "Boy and Girl" ad. The white binding ad not only was superior in the initial impact score and the post-readership score but also in the number of post cards returned.

The succeeding study assessed the relative effectiveness of a full color advertisement compared with a black and white one. Black and white advertising is much cheaper than color advertising. Hence, it is possible that even if black and white ads

**Table 15   Pupil Responses and Card Return to Two Split-run Encyclopedia Ads**

|  | Pupil-Response Scores | | | |
| --- | --- | --- | --- | --- |
|  | Initial Impact | Post-Readership | Total | Lead Performance |
| Control Boy and Girl Red books | 9 | 4 | 13 | 100% |
| Test Knowledge | 6 | 4 | 10 | 99% |

returned fewer post cards, the cost per post card might be lower for the black and white ads than for the color ads. Table 17 depicts the pupil response scores and the post card returns for

**Table 16   Pupil Responses and Card Return to Two Split-run Encyclopedia Ads**

|  | Pupil-Response Scores | | | |
| --- | --- | --- | --- | --- |
|  | Initial Impact | Post-Readership | Total | Lead Performance |
| Control Boy and Girl Red books | 9 | 4 | 13 | 100% |
| Test Boy and Girl White books | 11 | 13 | 24 | 115% |

these two ads. For all three criteria, the full color ad "Classroom" was superior to the black and white "Why buy?" The difference in the effectiveness was nearly the same as the cost difference, that is, black and white ads cost about 70 per cent of what it costs for color ads. Therefore, there was no cost efficiency achieved in running black and white ads.

The next study compared the "Family Telescope" ad with white bound books with four other ads, all run simultaneously. The "Family Telescope" ad was split run with one of the test ads in four different regional editions of the same publication. Therefore, the number of post cards received by "Family Telescope" differed for each region. Unfortunately, by the time this study was conducted, in 1965, the "Family Telescope" ad had been circulating for three years and was, so to speak, "worn out." It produced negative pupil response scores. Even so, it is possible to compare the relative effectiveness of the other four ads. Table

**Table 17    Pupil Responses and Card Return to Two Split-run Encyclopedia Ads**

|  | Pupil-Response Scores | | | Lead Performance |
|---|---|---|---|---|
|  | Initial Impact | Post-Readership | Total |  |
| Control Classroom | 12 | 11 | 23 | 100% |
| Test Why buy? | 2 | 8 | 10 | 70% |

18 shows the results for each test of the pupil scores and the post card performance in comparison with the "Family Telescope" post card performance in the particular regional edition in which it had been run. The first test ad, "Dennis," used the cartoon character. The second test ad, "Munsters," used the characters of that name. The third, "Danny Kaye," was illustrated by the well-known personality. The final test ad utilized an unusual illustration for the headline "Hiccups." All four of these ads showed higher pupil scores in initial impact, post-readership, and greater number of post card returns. While the pupil scores for the "Munster" and "Hiccups" ads were not significantly different from those for the control ad, they did nevertheless predict the greater post card lead in both cases. In the case of the "Hiccups" ad the post card data were regarded with caution since they were

based on a rather small sample of readers. The three test ads, of course, cannot be compared with each other because they were split-run with "Family Telescope" in different regions of the country.

**Table 18   Pupil Responses and Card Return to Four Series of Simultaneous Split-run Encyclopedia Ads**

| | Pupil-Response Scores | | | |
| | Initial Impact | Post-Readership | Total | Lead Performance |
|---|---|---|---|---|
| Control Family Telescope White books | −9 | −5 | −14 | 100% |
| Test Dennis | 10 | 10 | 20 | 114% |
| Control Family Telescope White books | −9 | −5 | −14 | 100% |
| Test Munsters | 4 | 1 | 5 | 108% |
| Control Family Telescope White books | −9 | −5 | −14 | 100% |
| Test Danny Kaye | 1 | 11 | 12 | 107% |
| Control Family Telescope White books | −9 | −5 | −14 | 100% |
| Test Hiccups | 0 | 8 | 8 | 116% |

The last test compared the "Boy and Girl" ad with white book bindings, with a test ad called "Wide Span of Books." Its principal illustration was the set of *Encyclopaedia Britannica.* The "Boy and Girl" was by that time also an ad that had been in circulation for some time. As Table 19 shows, it received negative initial and post-readership pupil scores. The test ad also received a negative initial pupil score but achieved a very slight positive score on the post-readership test. It turned out that it pulled in significantly more post cards.

**Table 19   Pupil Responses and Card Return to Two Split-run Encyclopedia Ads**

|  | Pupil-Response Scores | | | |
|---|---|---|---|---|
|  | Initial Impact | Post- Readership | Total | Lead Performance |
| Control Boy and Girl  White books | −6 | −3 | −9 | 100% |
| Test  Wide Span of Books | −7 | 1 | −6 | 111% |

As a result of these studies, it became clear that even differences in pupil response scores that were not statistically significant would predict correctly the superior post card performance of the ads in question. While the pupil response scores in either the initial impact situation or in the post-readership situation do correctly show which ad will be superior, they do not indicate precisely how great the difference will be. As would be expected, the post-readership scores tended to indicate more closely than did the initial impact scores the relative effectiveness of the ads studied.

In addition, the comparison of the effectiveness of the pupil response technique with several other methods of pretesting ads showed it to be more effective in predicting the post card performance of ads. This method of pretesting ads proved to have a considerable cost advantage because while the split run technique gives an objective measure of ad performance it is time consuming and costly. For one thing, it takes several months to receive the post cards, whereas the data are collected immediately with the pupil response technique. Also, the use of the pupil technique permits freer rein in experimentation with radical departures in advertising that would otherwise be discouraged because of the cost penalty incurred if a new ad should perform very poorly in returning post cards. With the pupil technique, a larger number of potential new advertisements may be screened and those producing the highest pupil scores can then be split-run.

Further studies as to whether there are regional differences in pupil and post card response to the ads were planned by Interpublic. Also, the predictive power of the pupil response was tested with respect to products, packages, basic advertising concepts, outdoor advertising, advertising at the point of purchase, and direct mail.

While we continued our basic research which included several students at the University of Chicago working on their Ph.D. degree theses on some aspects of pupil measurement, work continued at the Interpublic perception laboratory on various packaging and advertising materials. In a small way some studies were actually sold to outside clients. These were, however, not too frequent because while the basic technique was quite appealing when discussed with the client, it did not always result in an enthusiastic response as far as paying for some research was concerned. By that time we had a fair amount of basic information which indicated to us that the pupil response could be used to predict advertising success and perhaps even the success of the marketing of items such as wrist watches, watch bands, silverware, greeting cards, and so on. It obviously would be quite useful in terms of eliminating the really bad possibilities.

Let us take an example. When one puts out a line of wristbands for watches, it costs as much to prepare the dies for a poorly selling wristband as it does for one that will sell well. It is extremely useful for the manufacturer to know ahead of time that a certain pattern just is not going to be accepted by the public and that another one will do very well. So the strategy of those individuals who were responsible for selling this research possibility was to emphasize that even if the pupil response did nothing more than pick out the "dogs," it would have achieved a useful function which might save a great deal of money for the corporation.

In the meantime it seemed appropriate to Marion Harper that the rest of the organization, at least that part involved in marketing research, should hear about our perception research in some greater detail. The pupil apparatus which I had designed was named the "Eye Camera" by that organization. I have often thought that it would be difficult to imagine a more unfortunate choice, but for some reason, since I did not come up with any better alternative, this term has stuck. As far as I know it is still being used by Interpublic.

The big day came when I talked to the entire marketing organization in one of the ballrooms of the Waldorf Astoria. I was the only speaker. I began my address to these approximately 200 researchers by giving the title of my talk. Unhappily, I chose as a title "Ask Them No Questions and They'll Tell You No Lies." I then proceeded to talk about my own experiences quite briefly as an animal psychologist in which I had worked with perceptual problems and obviously where no questions were possible. I then discussed in some detail the origin and some of the basic research findings as well as our earlier marketing and advertising applications concerning the pupil response. I always get a good indication of how well I am doing whenever I lecture to a group. Feedback from watching the audience lets me know whether the direction I am taking and the kind of material I am presenting is going over well or whether it is falling with a dull thud. The response I noticed on the faces was worse than usual, and as I talked I realized what I was doing. I was telling a great many people whose livelihood depended on the use of questionnaires and interview material that what they were doing was essentially getting them as much misinformation as information, and that I had a technique which, when it was ultimately developed, would put them out of business. After the audience had sat through my talk with stony faces, the end came unmercifully. Although I do not remember precisely, I have a feeling that there was no applause but that everyone got up and walked out of the room. it was interesting that no one came up to ask me questions, and as far as I remember no one ever came up to the perception lab to see what was going on. This, in spite of the fact that it appeared to me that our pupil technique should be of interest to anyone in the business of pretesting advertising material and marketing possibilities.

I have been encouraged, however, by the fact that pupillomet-rics is still being used in the development of advertising materials.

I have talked about the attitude that academic colleagues present to those of us who are occasionally in contact with Madison Avenue. What I have neglected to state is that the problems are by no means confined to the academic community. It was true also with some of the people working at Interpublic. Although my status as an academic consultant was clear, it turned out that there was some resistance to the use of the pupil technique. Sometimes it took the following form. Instead of developing the sales techniques to sell this research service, the potential salesmen and directors of research activities would try to be helpful in "improving" the equipment and procedure. As Russell Schneider, one of my friends in the organization once remarked, "It looks as though everyone here is trying to reinvent the wheel." In some respects it was almost ludicrous. I remember a long memo from one of these staff members in which several suggestions about improving the apparatus were made including the fact that the light which is in the apparatus and which serves the double function of illuminating the eye for photographing and reducing the pupil size to approximately half its total possible size—to about 4 to 4½ millimeters—be eliminated because it would then be more comfortable for the subject.

Also, it was annoying that when a client was apparently all set to purchase the necessary research which would involve the pupil technique, one of the superiors would suggest another, perhaps his pet one, and this would then be used instead of the pupil response technique. I had no financial interest in the sale of this research since I was getting no royalties on the volume of research, but I was always interested in the results when we tested something new. Such knowledge as to what would be the result when a package to be tested, for example, had a picture of a baby's face on it, was very important because it would give us additional information to add to our stock of basic knowledge which we got from the work in our own laboratory.

The only conclusion I could come to finally was that there is little basic difference as far as people are concerned, whatever the organization in which one finds one's self. It is only the difference in the basic environment itself, and I thank heaven for the academic environment which, while it is a far cry from the Ivory Tower that some of the public assume it to be, is still one of the last refuges for free and unshackled enterprise. I do not mean to philosophize about this. I know that in some educational institutions, particularly those which are state-supported, there is a great deal of pressure exerted by the administration of the state or by the public which supports it. I am speaking only of the one university I know extremely well and I find it unique.

As our work continued and we accumulated more and more information and skill in the presentation of such materials and in the evaluation of the responses, I was told by several of the responsible people at Interpublic that what would really make a difference would be to be able to apply this technique to television commercials and the pretesting of them. I thought that was fine but the difficulties of presenting such materials in a pupillometric assessment were great. Anyone can see that as you watch a television set in a dark room, there are constant changes of illumination as the television commercial unfolds or as the television show proceeds. In fact, one can see the room suddenly get light and dark because the television screen itself throws out a great deal of light. This would mean that any changes which might be produced by the inherent emotional impact or interest in the commercial itself would be completely obscured by the tremendous pupil changes which would rather uniformly result from the changes in brightness. In other words, whenever the screen got brighter the pupil would get smaller, and if one did not take brightness into account, one would say this is a low interest or negative interest part of the commercial. As the screen got darker, the pupils would get bigger and it would then be interpreted as being positive or emotionally appealing.

One day, however, the very simple answer came to me. Instead of using the television screen, we could use a rear projection screen, just as we had done with the slides. On the motion picture projector we could have a photocell and light source which would scan the film as it entered the projection gate, and at the same time activate an iris diaphragm in front of the motion picture projector lens. It would be so wired that whenever the motion picture film got bright, a greater amount of photocell activity would result and it would close down the aperture of the iris diaphragm in front of the lens. It would thus effectively reduce the amount of light falling on the screen. As the motion picture material became more opaque, potentially producing a darker image, less light falling on the photocell would cause the iris diaphragm to open up toward its maximum, letting more light from the projector on the screen. By proper control of this system, we were able to produce a motion picture projector which would take any television commercial and essentially "smooth out" the brightness of the film so that the person viewing the commercial would receive very little change in overall brightness, just as in the past we had been able to control the brightness of slides. Niles Bernick built the prototype of this equipment.

This was a happy day for Interpublic. It was also a happy day for us because we had wanted to use material more stimulating than could be provided by a still photograph. We had thought of all sorts of possibilities. For instance, social interaction between people, could be presented in this way to elicit larger pupil responses than would be possible by use of still photographs.

For our first test I chose to use a commercial put out by the Anheuser Busch Brewing Company. This was a 60-second film which had several interesting scenes of skiers at the beginning, but near the middle there was a shot of a young woman in a bathing suit coming out of the water directly toward the camera, in a head-on, full-breasted view. Then, for the remainder of the film, there was talk about Busch Bavarian beer and its remarkable thirst-quenching quality. We used a total of only 16 subjects in our first study. Routinely in the experimental studies involving packaging advertising and new television commercials, 100 and sometimes more subjects are used. But the results obtained with our first 16 subjects were so interesting that we decided to go ahead and make a demonstration film showing the television commercial and superimposed upon it the second-by-second graphic response of the eye pupils of the 16 subjects.

One could then watch as the graph showing the pupil change recorded exactly what happened at any particular point in the commercial. When we first showed the film in a session at the Waldorf Astoria, it was a howling success. As the breasts of the

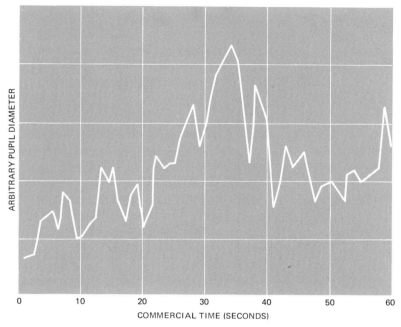

**Figure 25**   Average second-by-second pupil size of subjects during the one-minute viewing of a Busch Bavarian beer commercial. In general the pupil size increased during the first 30 seconds of the commercial and then dramatically increased when the girl emerged from the water. (Reprinted from ". . . in the eye of the beholder." Published in *Sponsor*, December 28, 1964.)

lady came into view the pupil curve shot up and the audience roared. I remember Marion Harper's exclamation—"Hot Dog!" It is in fact a compelling thing to see this animated "Interest Track," as it has been trademarked by Interpublic, superimposed upon any sort of visual material in motion picture form.

## T.V. BRIGHTNESS STUDY

Early in the development of a suitable testing technique for television commercials many questions were asked relating to the brightness changes within the television commercial. Under the auspices of Interpublic we decided to see whether or not we could get a definitive answer to this particular problem. We chose a television commercial which lasted for 60 seconds and which had rather marked brightness changes throughout the 60-second period. A brightness film was produced. This film was made by projecting the motion picture film of the television commercial against a diffusing screen and photographing this screen which now had no pattern on it but changed continually in brightness as the film unrolled. This film allowed us to present to the subjects merely the continuous changes in brightness of the television commercial without the presentation of any of the material which was involved in the picture part of the commercial.

A total of 50 subjects was used and they were shown three sequences of 60 seconds each, in succession. First, each half of the group saw this brightness field presentation preceded by a control so that changes from the neutral brightness could be later measured. One-half of the subjects then saw the actual television commercial with brightness controlled by means of the automatic diaphragm which I had devised. Following this, they saw the same commercial again, out of focus, but without controlling the brightness levels of the commercial itself. This was called the "brightness" film. The other 25 women were first shown the controlled brightness television commercial and finally, in the same test session, the uncontrolled television commercial—uncontrolled, that is, for brightness.

The results gave a very clear indication that changes in brightness were not producing the results which were obtained as far as the pupil responses were concerned for the showing of this particular television commercial. First of all, for the "brightness" film alone, I had a relatively continuous negative response except for the first momentary constriction which took place within a few seconds and was due to the fact that there was a bright opening for the film. Although fluctuations continually occurred, this continuous negative response showed a steady downward trend all the way to the end of the "brightness field" commercial. In fact, during the last several seconds of the commercial, the response averaged about 4 per cent constriction.

In marked contrast was the result of showing either of the two other films. In fact, the commercial not controlled for brightness showed the greatest amount of deviation. It reached a high point of 10 per cent at 30 seconds from the beginning, and toward the end of the commercial at about 55 seconds, reached a low point of 2 per cent constriction. It is also clear that by and large the effect of the brightness changes can be superimposed on the interest value aroused by that particular commercial. For example, we can see a peaking of response during the commercial; that is, the greatest increase in pupil diameter occurred at a point of about 30 seconds, both in the brightness field and in the uncontrolled brightness commercial. Similarly, excluding the initial constriction caused by the great change in light intensity occurring at about 52 or 55 seconds from the beginning, the lowest point in the commercial came at the same time as the constriction of over 5 per cent when the brightness field alone was shown to the subject.

Even more clear is the response from second 17 to second 22, when the brightness level decreased in the brightness field and dilation results. There is a constriction for that television commercial where the brightness remains relatively constant and is controlled. This can obviously only be interpreted as a decrease in interest during that period, if not in fact a negative response, since it reaches a zero point and goes slightly below the normal control line—thus offering additional evidence for the effectiveness of the interest aspect of the material which is presented to the subject and which is what we want to measure.

With the control of brightness, however, there are real discrepancies between the two interest tracks. One such case occurs, starting at 13 seconds, when the response in the controlled brightness condition increased for 4 or 5 seconds, whereas in the uncontrolled commercial the response drops markedly, over 4 per cent. This was, then, a conclusive, perhaps tautological, demonstration to us that brightness alone, although it could cause differences in pupil response, obviously was not involved when it was controlled. In further tests using the same television commercial, we were able to control brightness to an almost absolute level by means of recording the television commercial on video tape and then, by proper manipulation get an almost even flow of brightness from the beginning to the end of the commercial. This resulted in a response which did not show any of the influences we had obtained previously for brightness changes. This last study, which was done in our own

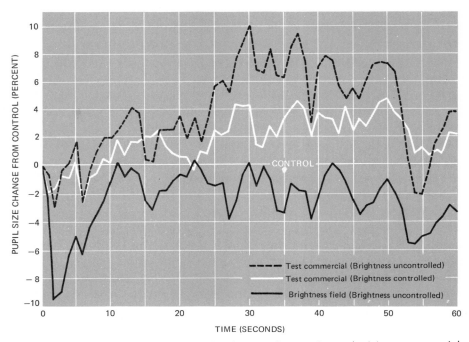

**Figure 26**    Pupil size response to brightness changes in a television commercial which was projected on the viewing screen completely out of focus so that only light changes could be seen. The actual commercial was also shown with brightness controlled and uncontrolled. It appears that light changes alone are generally boring to subjects, since there is a gradual decrease in pupil size during the viewing.

laboratory, made it evident that in order to work adequately with television commercials and television shows as stimuli for testing procedures, the maximum possible elimination of brightness changes would have to be achieved.

I recommended to Interpublic that all such material should, as soon as possible, be shown only on video tape. There was an additional good feature to such a procedure—the subject could view the commercial or the television show on a small television set which could be placed at the same point where the screen ordinarily was placed in the apparatus. We thus had a much more normal situation in that the subject was looking at a small television set and seeing what he might be likely to see at home, rather than having a somewhat artificial situation by projecting a motion picture on the back of the screen, as we had been doing heretofore. This procedure was then used in three major laboratory operations by Interpublic: one in Paramus, New Jersey, one in Chicago, and one in Los Angeles. The results so far have shown conclusively that this was the proper step to take.

The "Interest Track" used by Interpublic permits a detailed diagnosis of the effectiveness of the various portions of a commercial. Questions regarding the nature of the "sell" and "entertainment" portions of the commercial, for example, can be raised and studied. For instance, it may be decided to place the "sell" closer to a high interest point as a result of the "Interest Track" analysis. It can be used to determine the relative effectiveness of various ten-second lead-ins to the "sell" portion, or for picking out the best of a long commercial for reduction into a shorter one. As is well known, the primary function of a commercial is to get and to keep the viewer's attention. If the interest of the viewer is low, then it is clear that the viewer may "turn off" not only himself, but also the channel or the T.V. set.

This technique also permits the assessment of the pupil response as a function of the viewer. For example, it is common to compare the responses of men with those of women. Thus, if a commercial is directed toward a particular kind of audience, it becomes possible to assess the effect of the commercial on that audience. This type of application is shown in Figure 27, which depicts the response of men and of women to a food commercial. The "sell" portion of the commercial was in the middle. At this point, the interest of the males, which had been higher than that of the females, dropped sharply to the female level, while the females' interest was maintained.

A comparison of different commercials is also obtained with the "Interest Track" technique. Figures 28 and 29 show the comparative pupil responses for two commercials for a washday product. The first commercial aroused more interest during its first half than the second commercial did, while the second aroused more interest during its second half than the first one did. The pupil response has also been found to be more effective in discriminating commercials in interest value than the verbal responses obtained by means of interviewing the subjects. For example, in another of Interpublic's studies conducted by Her-

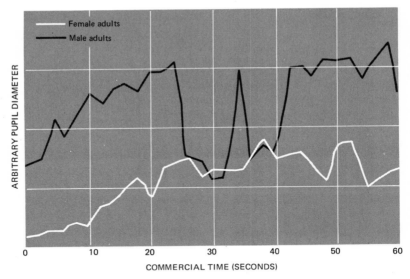

**Figure 27** A commercial for a food product elicited different pupil responses from men and women. The "sell" part occurred in the middle of the commercial, upon which the men showed a sharp drop in pupil size while the women maintained interest. This graph also depicts the usual tendency of men to have greater pupil responses than women to the interest portion of the commercial. (Reprinted from ". . . in the eye of the beholder." Published in *Sponsor*, December 28, 1964.)

bert Krugman, women were shown two different laundry commercials. The women reported about the same degree of preference for them when interviewed after seeing them. However, the pupil response showed more dilation for one of them, demonstrating that the pupil response is a more sensitive method of determining the interest value of the commercials than is the verbal report of the viewers. This shows, once again, that very often people either are unable to assess the nature of their own feelings or are unable to report them precisely. The pupil response does not require that the person perform the measurement of his own response to the material in question.

A study by Interpublic of 160 different 60-second commercials, also conducted by Krugman, has shown that the subject's interest level appears to be determined very early during the exposure to the commercial. The peak response during the first 10 seconds of viewing has been found to correlate rather highly, +.83, with the

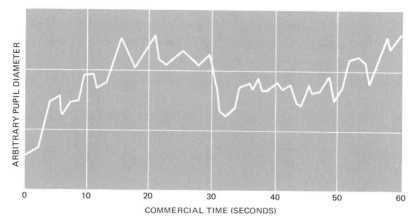

**Figure 28** Pupil responses of 74 housewives during the one-minute viewing of a laundry product commercial. This commercial aroused more interest during the first 30 seconds than during the second 30 seconds. (Reprinted from ". . . in the eye of the beholder." Published in *Sponsor*, December 28, 1964.)

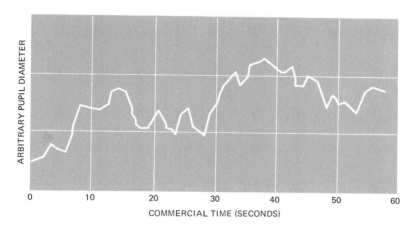

**Figure 29** Pupil responses of the same 74 housewives (as in Figure 28) to a different one-minute commercial for the same laundry product. This commercial was more effective during its last 30 seconds than during its first 30 seconds in eliciting positive responses from the housewives. (Reprinted from ". . . in the eye of the beholder." Published in *Sponsor*, December 28, 1964.)

average (mean) pupil response for the entire 60 seconds of the commercial.

Attitude measurement—that is, how effectively advertising

influences consumer attitudes toward products, and so on, using the "before-and-after" technique which we developed—has occupied a prominent place in Interpublic's use of the pupil response technique. They have been able to determine, for example, whether the increased favorable response to a product is greater after receiving information A or after receiving information B, C, D, or E.

The nature of the activities of the perception laboratory soon changed and the emphasis of the total operation was placed on the pretesting of television commercials. The number of television commercials which were pretested by Interpublic grew. Commercials by the dozen were tested each week. The perception laboratory was moved to an Interpublic operation in another building. As a result, the basic perceptual research project with which I had started was slowly but surely being abandoned because of the gold mine that was seen in this new development.

I talked to Mr. Harper about this problem and suggested that I disengage myself from the operation in order to return to the development of new techniques and new ideas along the lines which we had originally established. He agreed and told me, in words that I will never forget, "You tell me what you want to do and that's the way it's going to be." The following period of time proved to be very interesting because I had the opportunity to try some of these ideas. But, the unfortunate difficulty was that there were continuous problems which arose because of clients who had specific questions and it seemed as though most of my time, which was limited to a few days each month, was taken up in solving practical problems for the operation. Finally, a decision was made easier for me in terms of a way out when Mr. Harper left his position as chief of the operation in 1967. For me too, it was a good time to go.

Before I left the organization, however, and immediately after some of the earlier television commercials had been tested, I became concerned with an interesting problem. Perhaps it is fine to have high pupil responses to a television commercial because people find it entertaining, interesting, and appealing. But what does all this have to do with relating this response to a recognition of the product which was being advertised, and perhaps to increase its sales? For example, if you look at the pupil

responses to the Anheuser Busch commercial which we discussed, even though this commercial could be called very
successful in that it aroused a great deal of interest, we haven't
the slightest idea whether or not it has anything to do with
increasing one's favorable attitude toward the product which the
manufacturer is trying to sell.

At that point, I remembered that some of our basic research
dealt with changes in attitude as a result of exposure to
informational material. It seemed perfectly obvious to me that if
a television commercial were to do an effective job, it should
increase the positive attitude toward the product which was
advertised. In fact, I came up with the simple notion that *the
entire purpose of advertising material was to increase, maintain,
or create a positive interest in the product or concept which was
being promoted.* Why, then, I argued, couldn't one simply do a
"before and after" test? We could show the product at the
beginning of the session, then a television commercial for that
product, and finally the product again. If the commercial had a
positive effect on one's attitude toward it, then this is the best
that could be hoped for because nothing in the world, at least
not the television commercial, can physically take the customer
to the liquor store to buy that particular bottle of beer. I assumed
that if most things were equal, that is price, social status, and so
on, it would seem that creating a more favorable attitude toward
a product would obviously increase its likelihood of being sold.

I discussed this with some of the people at Interpublic, and
they saw the possibilities, so we began a series of studies along
this line. The term coined by Interpublic for this particular testing
situation was "added product appeal," or APA. I didn't think very
much of that because it made the assumption that something
was always added in the way of appeal, and we already had
evidence that in some instances a television commercial decreased the appeal of the product to the test subjects. I preferred
and suggested the term we still use, which is "relative attitude
change," or RAC.

In those instances in which we carried out basic research along
these lines, there seemed to be very little question about the
usefulness of this technique. It demanded careful procedures,
and in the field operations that were carried out by Interpublic

the careful controls which were possible in the laboratory situation apparently were not carried out. As a result of one study in which the outcome was not satisfactory to the client, Interpublic became disenchanted with the idea and Krugman recommended that this procedure no longer be used. I objected because it was obviously the most important way the pupil technique could be used to effectively determine and predict the advertising value of any material. I lost.

I have already mentioned that a test such as relative attitude change obviously depends on all things being equal. For example, it may be quite possible to have two commercials which deal with two different products, one a Rolls Royce, the other a standard automobile, and to show a much greater effectiveness of the Rolls Royce ad as compared to the one depicting the standard automobile. But the ultimate result, because of the price differential, will be much greater sales for the standard automobile and not much of an increase for the expensive Rolls Royce. There are obviously other problems. Sometimes the social values are such and pressures are sufficiently great to keep someone from buying something which he would dearly love to have. Because it is not the right thing to do, even though he has been stimulated by the advertising material, he simply will not buy it. And, of course, social values and pressures can work in the opposite direction to get people to buy things they dislike.

Then one day I came across what to me is perhaps the most astonishing problem about testing the effectiveness and the value of what has been created by the advertising world. In a series of discussions with some of the higher people in the organization, it suddenly became very obvious that no one really wanted a technique which would accurately and quantitatively determine just how good an advertising product was. The advertising agency did not want a valid and accurate yardstick which could be used to measure the quality of their work. After some reflection on this apparent anomaly, I suddenly got the insight that this was not so terribly unusual. Perhaps any of us who create something are much happier with the intangible judgments and values that can be made without having to know *precisely* just how good or how bad it is.

Let me give you two examples that may make this point clear.

All of us know that we are going to die some day. The current medical advances do not change this fact, but I doubt that there is any reader who wants to know his precise time of death. That kind of absolute and accurate prediction is not wanted.

Secondly, I thought of another possibility. Suppose some scientist came into my office and told me that he had an absolutely foolproof device into which we could place my research publications and those of my colleagues and then, on a meter in front of the apparatus, one could read the precise value of the research product in question on an accurate scale. I do not think I would want to make use of it. It is much better to assume that what one is doing is good, and one is happy when some colleagues approve. One can rationalize and dismiss those objectors and dissidents who do not find one's research contribution to be so valuable. Probably, the various creative people in the agency also preferred the kind of testing where final outcomes could always be rationalized.

So, instead, we continued with variations on the theme. Such questions came up as: What contribution does the sound track on a television commercial really make? How much good or damage is done by the pressuring voice of a certain kind of announcer? We found some interesting things. For example, the response to the sound track alone and the response to the visual part of the television commercial alone can be measured. When averaged out, we get a result which is very similar to that result which we obtained when both of these were presented simultaneously.

By far, the largest possible step forward in the evaluation of a television commercial and its effectiveness in relation to the product advertised is something that I have developed but which has not, to my knowledge, been used by any marketing research organization. This is something we might call "total evaluation technique" (TET). It is ultimately useful not only for television commercials but could be used with success in evaluating the impact of social interactions when shown on sound motion picture film or closed circuit television.

The TET technique consists of the following. A product is shown, and the pupil measurements are recorded. There is an intervening break of a minute or two. Now, again in a pupil apparatus but concurrent with the recording of the pupil response, a television commercial is shown to the subject. Simultaneously his Galvanic Skin Response is recorded. At the same time the subject is asked to move a lever, a stick which can be pushed either away from himself or toward himself, and which normally rests in a straight up position. The subject has only one task during this exposure period while he is shown the television commercial. He watches the commercial and if he likes what he sees, if it appeals to him, if he finds it pleasant, he pulls the stick toward him. He can pull it further toward him if it appeals to him more, or he can pull it less closely to him if it appeals only a little. If he finds it neutral he leaves the stick in the upright position. If he rejects the commercial he pushes it away from him. If he rejects it a great deal or completely, he pushes it as far as it will go. This information is simultaneously recorded on a running graph of the Galvanic Skin Response deflection. This will allow an evaluation on the graph, of an increase or decrease in emotional involvement with the television commercial by comparison with a baseline previously taken when the control is shown. And, of course, we have the pupil response. When this is over, we have a break of a couple of minutes, after which the subject is asked to again look at a picture of the product.

To make this study most complete the subject should return on the second day, when the same procedure is carried out. This has the advantage of covering all possible aspects of what is intended by the production and use of this television commercial. By the relative attitude change, we know how effective the television commercial was in producing or changing an attitude toward that product. By simultaneously having the GSR information, we can, as indicated in the previous chapter, make a further and more precise evaluation of the pupil response.

But, most important, we will know something about the nature of how the television commercial is actually perceived or how the subject feels it should be perceived. He may push the lever in such a way as to indicate that he likes the television commercial because he feels that this would please the experimenter and that he is "with it," while at the same time it may quite easily be shown that he finds the television commercial irritating. We would get this information because we might have a GSR response which is very high. This would denote an emotional response which could turn out to be negative because the pupil response might be much too low for the amount of GSR-recorded emotional upheaval which is taking place in the individual tested. Now all this sounds very nice, and it is, but there are still many difficulties that are encountered in carrying out research of this sort.

For example, although I have taken the bull by the horns and set up my own quantification scale so that I may *directly* compare the pupil response on a graph with the Galvanic Skin Response and with the voluntary response, the actual arguments which I used cannot yet be confidently published in a scientific journal. It is at this time merely an approximation. But I have used it to test ten commercials and have obtained results that seem reasonable and promising.

I want to mention one last research project because it gave me a great deal of pleasure and was interesting from the standpoint of making it very clear that either motion picture material or taped closed circuit television material and, even live action and interaction, can be used for the evaluation of social attitudes. In several instances Interpublic was asked by the major networks to pretest television pilot films. In each case I received a copy of the film and carried out some tests in our Chicago laboratory because I thought it would be very useful in the development of social attitude testing. Later I would be able to compare our results with the results obtained with large samples by Marplan. This information was made available to me for inspection. Some astonishing results came out of these studies. They were all half-hour shows, and we broke them up into two or three segments, because a half-hour session in the apparatus is a little too long and confining and because it is not unlike the "commercial break" in real television. Our first such attempt was the pretesting of a western pilot film.

There are several things about the results that demand immediate attention. One is that the pupil response, even when averaged for a large number of subjects, was phenomenal. It was higher than any responses we had ever gotten to our usual material. Generally one can scarcely expect more than a 5 per cent average pupil response for a hundred subjects to the most

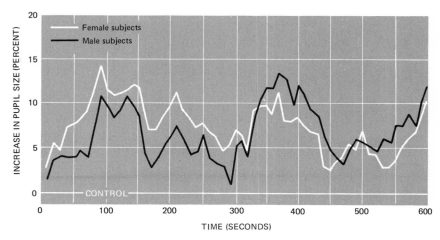

**Figure 30**   Average pupil changes for men and women viewing the first ten minutes of a T.V. pilot film.

interesting still picture during the ten-second period in which it is presented. For television commercials which ordinarily do not exceed one minute, the average response at its peak for the same number of subjects rarely exceeds 10 per cent. The average response for all our subjects at two dramatic peaks in the course of the half-hour show, however, went up to 25 per cent. This is a monumental increase when one considers that we are averaging out the responses of a great number of people. One of the subjects in that particular test situation gave a pupil response which is probably close to the limit physiologically. His actual increase, when the show reached its dramatic peak, was almost 90 per cent of the original diameter. In fact, the overall response of all subjects for the last ten minutes of the show, averages a solid 15 per cent increase in pupil diameter from the baseline. This is determined, as it is in all our studies, by a preceding control which is exposed for a period of ten seconds and which has the numerical notations on it.

Secondly, men and women do not necessarily have to have the same pupil responses for a television show. To be sure, they coincide roughly as the show changes its mood from one of a passive introduction to a boring scene, to action, to violence, to a dramatic peak, but sometimes for periods as long as a minute or two, the pupil responses can go in diametrically opposite directions. In one of the scenes the hero of the film is discovered in the midst of a crowd in a small town and, thought to be a murderer, is seized by some of the inhabitants of that town. As this is taking place, the hero with violent efforts wrenches himself free, kicks someone down, grabs a stick, and starts to beat his way through the crowd which is now gathering. This takes about 70 seconds. He is then caught and subdued.

Now the responses as shown in Figure 33 for the men are extremely instructive. From the point when the attempt is made to seize him and he makes his way through the crowd and appears to be able to get away, there is a steady increase in pupil diameter as the men watch the scene. It reaches a peak just as he is grabbed, and the instant he is actually caught the pupil response goes back down. All this is a change which is significant and quite large when one considers the number of subjects involved in this study. The pupil response for the women, however, is quite the opposite. From the moment that the hero

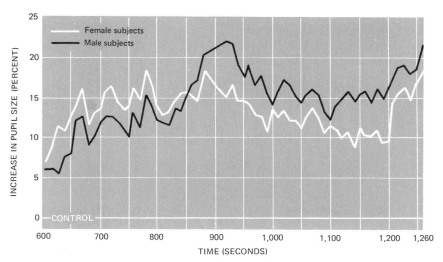

**Figure 31**   Pupil changes during the second ten-minute segment of the T.V. pilot film. Although the responses of the men and women are roughly similar, there is one minute (at about 900 seconds on the graph) during which the responses are diametrically opposed. This can be seen in greater detail in Figure 33.

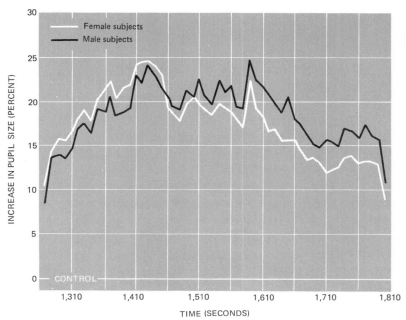

**Figure 32**   The responses to the concluding segment of a half-hour T.V. pilot film. The two climactic portions of this show are at 1430 and at 1590 seconds. These are also the points at which the pupils for both men and women reach their greatest diameter.

appears to be able to evade the clutches of his would-be captors, there is a steady downward trend in the pupil response—it continues to get smaller and only at that point where he is actually and clearly caught does the pupil response go up again. I have jokingly suggested to some of my audiences when I have lectured using this material that here we have an indication of a fundamental difference between men and women. The men like to see the man get away; the women like to see the man caught.

On the serious side, however, it is necessary to take into account differences in response such as men having larger pupil changes than women, when using a sample of both men and women for the pretesting of either television commercials or television shows. Otherwise, one can easily be misled and assume that the result indicates a greater appreciation or interest in the material on the part of men as compared to women. For example, in most of the cases in which the material is considered about equally interesting to both men and women, men indeed give larger pupil responses. Of course, this is not going to be the case if we deal with material which is directed to women more than to men. For example, men have bigger pupil responses in comparison with women when shown a picture of a female nude, while the opposite is true if the pictorial representation is that of a male nude.

It seems evident to me that the pupil response is not only extremely useful in evaluating an average response of a great number of individuals but also in assessing the idiosyncratic responses of a single individual. It would also be useful in a tremendous variety of possible areas that can be explored: the development of the interests of the child, the development of vocational interests and attitudes, the already mentioned social issues and problems, medical and mental health problems, and a host of other possibilities which I am sure the reader as well as I could sit down and enumerate by the hour.

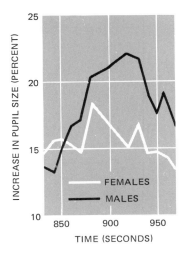

**Figure 33** Responses for men and women from 880 to 930 seconds show opposing trends. In this scene the hero of the story is about to be caught by a mob but kicks his way free. For the next 40 seconds it looks as though he may get away. During this time the men's pupils get bigger and the women's pupils decrease in diameter. When he is actually caught the men's pupils constrict sharply, while there is a brief period of dilation for the women subjects.

Thus we see that the pupil response has a usefulness that has never been fully utilized by advertising and marketing organizations. Contrary to a misleading article published in early 1974, in a popularized "psychology" magazine, it has not been a question of "oversell" but rather one of a lack of proper application of its potential.

# 12

# A Look to the Future

In recent years, pupillometric research in other laboratories has made several contributions to the study of attitudes, affect states, and nonverbal communication. The usefulness of some of these findings has been most encouraging. For example, Owen A. Kennedy recently completed a study in which pupil responses to alcoholic olfactory stimuli were investigated in alcoholics during rehabilitation treatment and upon follow-up after discharge. All subjects were tested biweekly for pupil responses to water and to their preferred alcoholic beverage. The pupillometric data indicated a diminution of pupillary dilation during the course of treatment—a phenomenon which suggests that the therapeutic impact of treatment is assessed by pupillometrics. In fact, a dramatic reduction of pupil dilation to the alcoholic stimulus occurred during the final weeks of the treatment program, thus indicating the importance of this period of treatment. Furthermore, pupil dilation to the alcoholic stimulus was significantly and positively correlated with recidivism. That is, the presence of dilation to the alcoholic odor prior to discharge from the treatment program was related to the likelihood of return for more treatment. Hence, it can serve as a signal indicating the need for continued treatment or intensive follow-up care.

Pupillometric evaluation of emotional affect has been used in another way by John W. Schweikert. He showed pictures of various vocations to high school and college students. It was found that the pupil response data provided a good index of the feelings of acceptance or rejection generated by the pictures.

Questionnaire responses correlated well with the pupil response data.

Pupil responses in social and sexual situations have continued to be studied. Hiram E. Fitzgerald found more pupil dilation by four-month-old infants to social stimuli than to nonsocial ones.

My own findings that introverts show stronger pupil responses to stimuli than do extraverts have been followed by several studies. While R. D. Francis and M. R. Kelly reported that neuroticism tendencies in normal subjects seemed to bear some relationship to pupil response style, Francis showed that subjects having strong pupil responses had higher neuroticism scores on a personality test. According to H. J. Eysenck neuroticism is closely related to the inherited lability of the autonomic nervous system. The Eysencks have demonstrated through their "lemon juice" test for extensiveness of salivary responsiveness, that introverts have greater autonomic lability. The introverts salivate more when real lemon juice is placed upon their tongue than do the extraverts, a finding very much in line with my pupil studies of introverts and extraverts. However, Francis did not find high pupil responsiveness to be associated with high introversion, and he did not report directly upon the data regarding the relative pupil responsiveness of subjects with high introversion scores.

Certainly it does appear that personality variables can influence pupil responses. For example, Loren J. Chapman, Jean P. Chapman, and Terry Brelje have reported that pupil dilation responses of young men to pictures of females tended to be inhibited by an aloof and reserved experimenter and to be facilitated by an easy-going and friendly experimenter. Lawrence M. Krueger also showed small inhibitory effects upon pupillary dilation responses of young men to female pictures through certain experimental settings.

The repression-sensitization concept has been studied in several pupillometric investigations. It is a scale constructed from other MMPI scales and has been found to relate to measures of inhibition-facilitation as described by Donn Byrne. Pavel Machotka in a study investigating pupillary responsiveness in relation to personality defenses and preferences for esthetic distortion, has suggested that "sensitizers" tended to choose distorted versions of sexually arousing pictures on the basis of their awareness of differences in the pictures' sexual arousal. "Repressors," he suggested, were not as aware of such sexual arousal and preferred less distortion in the sexually arousing pictures. Machotka did not present data upon the pupillary responsiveness of sensitizers and repressors. Lawrence R. Good and Richard H. Levin reported no effect of the repression-sensitization personality variable for magnitude of pupillary dilation and no evidence for dissimilarity in patterns of pupil reactions. Also, Roland H. Tanck and Paul R. Robbins found no relationship between scores on the repression-sensitization scale and pupillary dilation to a series of pictorial stimuli. The latter authors have suggested that the repression-sensitization scale may not adequately measure repression. Nevertheless Richard S. Fredericks found that sensitizers had greater dilation responses to pleasant pictorial stimuli than did the repressors, whereas the repressors had greater constriction responses to unpleasant stimuli.

Recently several interesting aspects of pupillary responses in relation to personality factors have been reported by Herbert Coverdale. He studied four personality groups involving extraversion, introversion, neuroticism, and stability. He found that "novelty" factors in pictorial stimuli were most related to the pupillary responses of all personality groups with the exception of the "stables." The pupillary behavior of the "stables" was most related to "complexity" factors in the pictorial stimuli. Neurotics also showed pupillary responses to "dynamism" and "personal relevance" factors, while extraverts showed pupillary responses to "potency" factors. Neurotics also showed a significantly higher frequency of pupillary constriction responses than did the other three personality groups.

In the area of sexual behavior, studies have been made which help in understanding the psychological dynamics which occur. I have already mentioned Atwood and Howell's study of pedophiliacs in comparison with sexually nondeviant men. New light upon sexual dynamics in paranoid schizophrenia appears to have been cast by Joseph A. Sheflin through pupillometrics. It has long been suggested that paranoid schizophrenics suffer from latent homosexuality. However, Sheflin found that both process and reactive schizophrenics showed more pupil dilation to pictures of women than to pictures of men, just as normal heterosexual males do.

The most pressing problem for the future development of pupillometrics is a two-fold one. First, we need quantification and the ability to accurately scale and evaluate the response. Secondly, we need more sophisticated equipment which will allow us to simply measure the pupil changes and, preferably, do this with a number or even a large number of subjects at one time.

As has been apparent throughout this book, we deal with pupil changes in terms of percentage of dilation and constriction. Let us say, for example, that a pupil is approximately 4 millimeters in size when the stimulus is first given to the subject, and that it dilates to 6 millimeters, therefore increasing 50 per cent in diameter, but nowhere near its physiological limit. A decrease of 2 millimeters would give us a constriction of 50 per cent. In the latter case we have a response that cannot exceed 50 per cent because the pupil just can't get any smaller. Dilation could however, be 100 per cent or more. According to some work that we have done, the optimum pupil size at which any stimulation should begin is probably quite close to 5½ millimeters in diameter. Now an increase of 50 per cent would bring the pupil up to about 8¼ millimeters, and a decrease of 50 per cent would bring it down to about 2¾ millimeters. This obviously achieves a greater amount of equality in the two-directional scaling system that we have been considering.

However, it isn't quite that easy. As earlier mentioned, human babies and children on the whole, have larger pupils than do teenagers; teenagers have larger pupils than middle-aged people; and middle-aged people have larger pupils than old people. There is a progressive decrease in pupil size throughout the life of a human being. There are exceptions to this, of course, but the statistical change is quite clear and according to some authorities it changes at the rate of about three-hundreths of a millimeter every year between the ages of 20 and 90 years.

Most important is the scaling of pupil dilation. Obviously, a 20 per cent increase in pupil diameter cannot merely be twice as great a response as a 10 per cent increase in diameter. It is easy to get that first 10 per cent change in pupil size, not so easy for the next 10 per cent increase, and so on, until we reach the absolute size limit where it is no longer physically possible to have any greater increase. So how should our scale be set?

One of the methods a scientist uses is to see whether a different function will fit such a scale, and one that he most often turns to is a logarithmic scale. If we have a logarithmic scale, then we get a situation in which it becomes harder and harder to add components until we flatten out into something that looks like infinity. In other words, we at first get a steep rise, a very quick response. Then it begins slowly to level off, and it levels off more and more until finally it just does not rise any more. It is perhaps just something like that which may be occurring in the pupil response. One way in which this may work is if it becomes possible to see whether or not a certain combination of stimuli gives us an additive effect.

Let us assume that the effects of a strong taste and a visual stimulus more or less support each other so that the total response is really additive, that is, a combination of the two. For example, we might get a 10 per cent increase in pupil diameter for a particular taste of a substance such as we have described in an earlier chapter, and we might also get a 10 per cent increase in pupil diameter for a certain visual stimulus. Now, a combination of the two might give us a score of perhaps 14 per cent increase in diameter, and we could see how well this would fit into our predetermined logarithmic scale. Of course, there is still the problem that there may not be a completely additive effect but, rather, a kind of partial summation of these two stimuli. These considerations are highly relevant to the effects of autonomic arousal in the determination of pupil size, as we discussed previously. Nevertheless, this is the general direction in which we have to go, and some of our results so far encourage us to feel that this might be the right track.

What can we expect, then, of the future as far as some of the problems to which the pupil technique may be directed are concerned? First, and probably foremost, would be the field of mental health and therapy. I have already discussed these possibilities in an earlier chapter, but I want to emphasize again that the intelligent use of the pupil methodology, along with other physiological measures and whatever questionnaire and interview material may be important, could constitute an extremely valuable tool in the understanding of such processes that may otherwise very easily resist the investigations of even the most competent therapists. This might be particularly true in the use of some of the drugs that have been involved in mental health care. It would seem extremely important, as long as these drugs do not in themselves intrinsically affect the pupil response, to determine their effectiveness in relation to changing the individual's attitudes or perceptions of the outside world. I have already stated that it is possible to determine, by means of the pupil response along with other measures, the extent of anxiety which is produced by certain visual material. We often have a patient who has an untoward amount of anxiety to certain types of subject matter which can be pictorially or in some other way presented to him. It would be very simple to test the effectiveness and even to time the onset of effectiveness of drugs that are being developed for the prevention of such anxiety. To my present knowledge, this area has not yet been touched. This technique is already being used to measure the progress and the direction of psychotherapy. I firmly believe that, with intelligent use, the opportunities for progress are quite great.

I have also mentioned the possible use of this technique in the determination of social attitudes that may resist the investigations of the experimenter when conventional techniques are used. This technique could prove to be extremely useful particularly in the area of attitude change and the sort of information and exposure that influence attitude change. It is, after all, no different, whether we are attempting to measure the effectiveness of advertising or some sort of political propaganda. We have already been able to clearly show the effectiveness of this kind of material when it's exposed to the subjects.

Hereto, the surface has not yet really been scratched but, as I have said before, a great deal depends on the experimenter's proficiency in *asking the right question.* It is not enough to do as some of the boys on Madison Avenue say, "Let's run it through the eye camera." You have to be specific in setting up the visual material, whether it is presented in pictures, in the printed word or possibly even by means of auditory input. The effects of brightness can never *entirely* be eliminated. All that we have been able to do is *minimize* the effects of brightness until the brightness differences in our research material can cause pupil changes of no more than plus or minus 1 per cent. Then when we are dealing with stimulating material—material which causes pupil changes of 10, 20, 30 per cent dilation in subjects, or constrictions of 10 per cent—we are obviously dealing with something that has nothing to do with mere brightness effects, all the vociferous arguments from some researchers to the contrary. In this area it would be extremely instructive to see what would occur if the material presented included, in addition to the kinds of things used so far, real "live" situations. For example, role playing could easily take place in another room and it could be observed by the subject while sitting in the experimental apparatus.

Another area in which we have made some small beginnings is the investigation of the pupil response on a developmental level. The youngest children from whom we have been able to get respectable pupil changes have been approximately three months old. In the two subjects, there was a clear indication that when the mother's face was presented to the child, the pupils increased more than they would in response to a man or to a strange woman. This was true for both of the subjects we used, and who make up our entire experimental population for that age level. It is not the simplest experimental procedure to get pupil responses from such young children, but I think it is possible to devise techniques which would allow the investigation of the pupil response from the first day of life. I scarcely need to point out that in this regard, the possibility of asking verbal questions of the young infant or child is obviously out of the question.

What we have done more extensively is to work with young children from the preschool level up through all ages. Niles Bernick did a doctoral thesis on psychosexual development during the childhood years and during adolescence. In this study, Bernick investigated the pupil responses of boys and girls to pictures of babies, mothers with babies, mothers with a girl or a boy, fathers with babies, fathers with a girl or a boy, girls, boys, men, and women. He also obtained verbal preferences from them by asking which pictures among those shown they liked the most and which they liked the least. All the children were students drawn from kindergarten and grades 1, 2, 4, 6, 8, 10, and 12, with approximately eight children of each sex in each grade.

The pupil responses elicited by the pictures in these boys and girls gave very different indications of what has long been assumed to be the social-sexual preferences of young children and adolescents. The boys showed a stronger pupil response to pictures of babies than to any other class of stimuli. They also showed more dilation to pictures of mothers than to pictures of fathers. The girls, on the other hand, showed more dilation to pictures of fathers than the boys did. Pictures of men and women elicited much less pupil dilation in boys and girls than did the pictures of babies, mothers, or fathers. Even with the smaller response to pictures of men and women, boys showed a stronger pupil dilation to the pictures of women than to the pictures of men, and the girls showed the opposite. It therefore appears that the pupil responses of boys and girls showed the same type of opposite sex interest as we found in adults in our very first research. This interest appears relatively constant with respect to peers, adults and parents from the age of 5 to 18 years.

Verbally expressed preferences of the children and adolescents for these same stimulus categories, however, conformed far more with the generally accepted beliefs of social preferences in children. The verbal data in general showed a same-sex preference contrary to the pupil data. In other words, boys said they preferred the pictures of the boys to the pictures of the girls, the pictures of the men to the pictures of the women, and so on; and the opposite was true for the girl subjects. Thus, the pupil response was quite the opposite of the verbal preferences. In addition, while the verbal preferences of the boys and girls for pictures of babies was relatively high, the verbal preference of boys for pictures of mothers was extremely low, and the verbal preference of girls for pictures of fathers was high. Although the verbal response data obtained by Bernick partially supported the general notion of a latency period in the psychosexual development of the child, the pupil response data did not at all. It is therefore possible that the so-called latency period may be no more than a reflection of social and cultural pressures upon the expression of verbal responses.

We have already shown that this is not an unusual phenomenon: we get very high agreement between pupil responses and expressed verbal preferences as long as the subject matter is relatively free from any kind of social pressure. The examples in point are the ones mentioned earlier in the book where we had tremendously high correlations between the pupil response to food pictures and the verbal rankings for them. The correlation between the pupil response and what a female subject said was low or even negative in dealing with photographs of the same and opposite sex, but in which the individuals represented were nude.

From the work that resulted in his thesis, Bernick concluded that "one of the peculiar rules of our social values system is that while girls are relatively free to become tomboys or father's girls, boys who are sissies or mother's boys are usually condemned by their age mates and adults as well. The girls' responses to the father appear to be the only socially accepted opposite sex preference in the system."

While the study on the psychosexual development of the child is obviously a simple beginning, it does point the way for what can be done, and I have every reason to believe that future investigations will be carried out. In some instances we might find quite the opposite results from those we anticipate. I do not doubt that this also will be the outcome if we investigate thoroughly and without fear, those problems which involve social attitudes all the way from our customs and culture to our prejudices and biases. In fact, with such a clear understanding as to what really happens, it could be that the way will be made easier for us to achieve the solutions which are so piously talked about by the politicians, the liberals, and the intellectuals, but where there seems to have been little progress.

In advertising and in marketing it may be possible to see many benefits if greater attention is paid to the possible usefulness of this technique in conjunction with others. A new era in advertising which does not include the noxious, raucous and otherwise unpleasant aspects of the media may be achieved. There is no

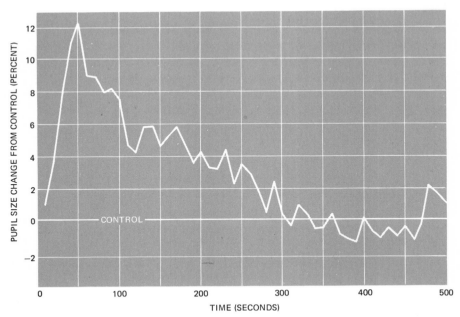

**Figure 34**   Pupil responses of women subjects during the first 500 seconds of the T.V. pilot film "The Hero." There is an immediate pupil dilation for the violent western scene. The pupil then returns to the baseline for the ensuing scenes which make the hero look like a bungling fool.

question that sensitive and sensible television commercials can be made. We have ample proof of this. The only problem is to convince the advertisers and perhaps have them convince themselves and their clients that such approaches can be even more effective than the techniques that have been tried.

In many respects much of what goes on in the development of advertising material is still the result of someone's hunch or intuition. Sometimes these hunches and intuitions are remarkably good, but not always. A complete or total evaluation, such as I discussed in the previous chapter, is the type of answer that should be sought if we are to talk about doing advertising research. Unfortunately, the climate is such that research is a magic word, and any advertising organization of any size has to have "research" whether they like it or not. In most cases, as far as I can tell in my association with the advertising business, the research results are accepted by clients or management if they are in accord with what they have already made up their minds to do, and are ignored if the results come out otherwise.

There is one area which is really not advertising or marketing but deals with the television medium itself. It is no big secret that when many people are asked the question of what is wrong with television, the answer is that it does not have enough of the right kinds of programs. If the person is asked what kind of program he would like to see on television, we often get answers that clearly

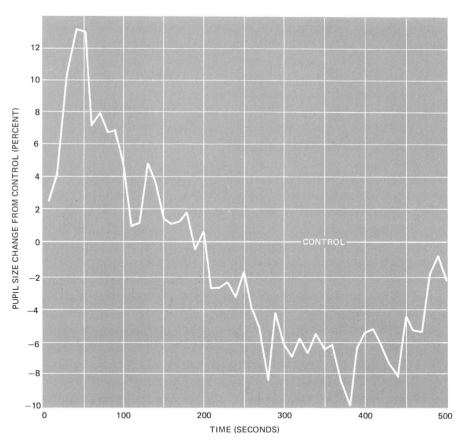

**Figure 35**  Pupil responses of men subjects to the same 500 seconds as in Figure 34, of the T.V. pilot "The Hero." The men have a much greater *negative* response to seeing a man pictured as a fool.

imply that educational television is what is really needed, and that programs should be interesting and contribute to our knowledge. Now, it turns out that this is distinctly untrue. By that I mean, it is *not* what people really want. The major networks have often presented television programs which were of superior quality and which were educational. They were, from any standpoint, interesting and worthwhile. The only trouble was that few people watched these programs. Obviously, this is an oversimplification, but I have seen many records of surveys which were taken when a good Shakespeare play was produced with the finest actors available, and which in the survey and rating lost out to quiz shows, a roller derby and other entertainment. So the question is to find out what people really like. If it could be done on a pretesting basis, the answers could be arrived at more easily and certainly much more economically.

Also, in areas where social pressures may not be too great, the information that we get from such physiological techniques as the pupil response should indicate quite clearly the type of programs that would be maximally interesting and therefore watched.

Another experiment in which private attitudes were revealed was shown when Interpublic was asked to evaluate some publicity by Metro-Goldwyn-Mayer for a motion picture starring Elizabeth Taylor and Richard Burton. We tested a number of still photographs that were to be used for publicity or advertising purposes in national magazines and newspapers. Contrary to our expectations, the greatest pupil responses were to those pictures which involved some sort of violence between Richard Burton and Elizabeth Taylor. They were not to pictures which showed Elizabeth Taylor in some seductive pose. I think this obviously reflects the spirit of our times and may well explain the contradictory results, that is, contradictory to our expectations. As experimenters, we may operate under the naïve assumption that these pictures ought to be frowned upon, or ought to be distasteful to the general public.

We have already begun some research in experimental esthetics. It is well-known that there are experts who proclaim that one thing is good and another is bad. Let us consider two designs. The expert will say A is good art and good design; B is bad. The question is, Why is it good or why is it bad? The art expert says that certain rules have been evolved by certain people and that is what makes A good and makes B bad. We have tried to test some of these sets of designs and the results are interesting.

In general, there are larger pupil dilations for those designs which are also picked by the experts to be better art. This is reminiscent of the silverware design study we described earlier. The pupil responses, by the way, are not necessarily in agreement with the verbal responses of individuals who may know little or nothing about art and who are unable to really verbalize the preferences which their eyes are able to show.

This experimental approach to esthetics is but one of the aspects of the research that can be done in areas which were heretofore almost impossible to crack and in which I think a dent can be made. I think it will be extremely useful and here, perhaps, we come to the important part of what this is all about. What can pupillometrics do for you? I think the answer is that it may help in esthetic problems such as what we really would like to have or see in our rooms, in our houses; what kinds of houses we want and even how a city should be planned. For too long the planning for all of these has been done largely by "experts" who may have a grand time producing creations which may not be suitable for the majority of the people who have to live with them. Or, for example, in the selection of materials for clothes, the style trends both for men's and women's fashions could be evaluated by screening techniques that would give some guidance as to the direction in which planning should go. And, lastly, there is a possibility that the interests of a child could be determined at the time when it is still optimal to train him for the problems that face him in the world. It is not enough to know the expressed preferences of the child as to what he thinks he wants to do because too often children are confused and influenced by what society expects of them. This is true also in the determination of vocational interests which might give a much better and more equitable integration of talent into our society.

All in all, I am very optimistic about the future prospects of pupillometrics, particularly in alliance with other psychosensory measures. I believe that new and useful applications will continue to be made, and that the ones already being utilized will promote much greater understanding of human behavior, particularly in areas involving mental processing, affect, nonverbal communication, and therapy.

I would like to end this book by suggesting to the reader that he take a look at the world around him and study the pupil phenomenon for himself. It is possible to do this because pupil size changes serve as a form of nonverbal communication. Thus, readers can easily set out to find what people "know" about the size of eye pupils, how they react to and interpret differences in eye pupil sizes.

It is simple to make preliminary explorations by studying artistic representations of eye pupils in faces portraying different emotions and different characters. Children's books are a good source of such illustrations. There, one can find out how the pupils are shown in faces picturing "innocence," "greed," or "evil." Interestingly, there seems to be a difference between the older and the newer children's books in the portrayal of eye pupils. The older books tend to show the pupils in most expressions whereas the modern ones seldom tend to show pupils.

Examples of differential pupil size representation can be found in some children's books. It would appear that illustrators have some kind of "knowledge" as to what pupils should be like for different expressions.

Recently I made up an extremely simple experiment that is as uncomplicated as my very first experiment in which I showed pictures to Dr. James Polt by holding them above my head. In this recent experiment I drew two schematic outline faces which were about three-quarters natural size. One face was smiling and the other was angry. In both pictures the eye pupils were left blank. I showed these two faces to people and gave them a No. 2 pencil with an eraser on it. I said to them, "Draw in the size pupil you think best fits the face." I immediately got very interesting results from the 20 people to whom I showed these pictures.

Among these 20 people there were 10 men and 10 women. I found that the pupils drawn by both the men and the women for the "happy" face were larger than the ones they drew for the "angry" face. Table 20 shows the average sizes of the actual pupils drawn by the men and women for the faces. There is no significant difference between the men and women in the pupil sizes that they drew for the two faces.

I became excited by getting such clear-cut findings from the 20 subjects who had never been told anything about pupil size change phenomena. I realized once again that the "average person" often can know the answers to questions long before the "experts" go through their costly research.

**Table 20   Mean Actual Pupils Drawn by 20 Subjects (in mm)**

|  | Face | |
|---|---|---|
|  | **Happy** | **Angry** |
| Men | 4 | 2.9 |
| Women | 4.5 | 2.8 |

Because this experiment is so easy to do I have provided the materials for doing it in this book. By using the ten sets of "angry" and "happy" pictures at the end of this book (slightly smaller than the ones I made up), the reader can readily test relatives or acquaintances to find out what they "know" about the meaning of different eye pupil sizes. Some of the findings that one can discover by doing such research turn out to be very interesting. For example, some time after I had done the above experiment, I showed the two schematic faces to a ten-year-old boy. He drew a larger pupil for the "happy" face than for the "angry" face. I asked him why he had done that and he replied, "Well, everybody knows they're supposed to be that way."

Several students in my laboratory are currently investigating this aspect of pupillometrics. One of them, James Dickson McLean, has just completed his Ph.D. dissertation on the social significance of the eye pupil (McLean, 1974). This dissertation concerned itself with the developmental aspect of the knowledge that people seem to have about the size of pupils in relation to age, emotion, and sex of faces. He worked with individuals from age 6 to 22 years, showing them schematic faces differing in pupil sizes. He found that the turning point for the social meaning of different sized pupils occurred at the age of 14 years.

Of particular interest among McLean's findings is that the blue-eyed subjects were better at judging *opposite* sex pictures than the brown-eyed subjects were at judging *same* sex pictures.

This particular finding has been corroborated by the work of another doctoral student of mine, Angelique Sallas. She has been studying expected pupil sizes for photographed faces having different emotional expressions. She has already found, by using paired photographs differing in pupil sizes, that her blue-eyed subjects judged in accordance with all previous results which we have obtained, when they looked at opposite sex pictures. Brown-eyed subjects showed least discrimination in judging same sex faces. The subjects in Sallas's research were found to associate large pupils with moods such as approachable, friendly, happy, and contented, while they associated small pupils with such moods as sinister, sly, disapproving, and sad.

In another study by one of my students, Patrick Shrout, six copies of a schematic face were given to 34 subjects who knew nothing about pupil research. The schematic faces contained only the face outline, the nose, eyes without pupils, and the hairline (see Figure 36). Subjects were asked to draw in the missing parts on the faces that would make them appropriately express six different moods: very happy, very tired, displeased, complacent, bored, and very angry and threatening.

When we analyzed the sizes of the pupils drawn into the faces with the different moods, the results were in close agreement with the other studies I have just discussed. The faces were distinct from each other with respect to the pupil sizes the subjects gave them. In addition, the "very happy" face had significantly larger sketched-in pupils in comparison with the "displeased," "bored," and "very tired" faces. One very interesting aspect of Shrout's data was that the "very angry and threatening" mood was portrayed with quite large pupils, second only to those for "very happy," even though the face resembled "displeased" with respect to the frowns and darkened brows which the subjects drew into these faces. Thus, in this study subjects were able to differentiate between two moods which were mixed together in the frowning schematic face I used in my own earlier study. Furthermore, Shrout's subjects correctly chose the more aroused mood to give larger pupils (a sign of bodily

**Figure 36** Schematic face given to the subjects who were asked to draw in the missing parts to make the face convey six given moods.

arousal), even though they were not consciously aware of the functioning of the pupil!

There is only one disturbing thought that has entered my mind about the future years of pupillometrics. This is the problem of its potential abuse in the invasion of privacy. Periodically I have been asked to cooperate in using pupillometrics in enforced "lie detection" situations. I have refused each time. I hope that the use of pupillometric techniques will find its greatest benefits in

**Figure 37a**   The two pictures given to subjects to draw in appropriate pupils.

**Figure 37b**   Average pupil sizes drawn into schematic faces by 10 men and women. They were given the two pictures with the pupils missing and asked to draw in the appropriate sized pupils for the expression shown. Fifteen out of 20 persons drew larger pupils into the "happy" face than into the "angry" face.

the determination of treatment effectiveness, in the measurement of attitude changes, in the assessment of mental processing, and in any other aspect of human behavior which would benefit our total society.

# 13

# Appendix: How Pupils Are Measured

Since light does affect pupil size, we have to control it very carefully if we are to find out the effects of mental and emotional events or any kind of nonvisual event on a person's pupil size.

The basic method in our research is to keep the brightness of light at the exact same level. This is easy enough to do if we are asking our subjects to perform mental or muscular tasks, to listen to sounds or to taste or smell objects. But it is not so easy when we are attempting to assess a subject's emotional or intellectual responses to pictorial or other visual material.

In such cases, the total brightness of the visual material must be placed at a certain level. Generally speaking, we use a brightness level which will maintain the subjects' pupils at a size that will permit either dilation or contraction to occur. In addition, we have found that it is necessary to prevent excessive dark-light contrast in the visual material. Even though it would not seem so obvious that dark-light contrast could influence the response of the eye pupil to light conditions, we have found that this is indeed the case. For example, we showed some subjects a picture of a square on a plain background. We could construct pictures in which the square was light and the background dark, or in which the square was dark and the background light, and yet both had the same total amount of brightness. Different subjects' pupils reacted in different ways to this variation in contrast. Hence it appears that areas of darkness affect pupil size in different ways when they are in different portions—in the center or near the edge—of the visual field.

Therefore we prepare the pictures we use for our studies according to a thorough and painstaking procedure. We have developed techniques of making all our slides of these pictures fall within a relatively limited range of total brightness and of controlling the amount of contrast within each one. Through photographic techniques and artistic work we are able to accomplish this. Each slide, furthermore, is matched extremely closely in total brightness value with a "control" slide consisting of a gray area having five numerals from one through five placed on it, or an "x" in the middle (see Figure 6). The change in the size of the pupil when the picture is being seen thus measures the person's reaction to the picture itself rather than to the overall brightness or dark-light contrasts within the picture. The quality of the slides used is further standardized by the fact that we always use Kodachrome Type 2 tungsten film for making them. Those readers who are interested in knowing all the exact details of how we make our slides may read the comprehensive chapter appearing on this subject in *Handbook of Psychophysiology*, edited by Norman Greenfield and Richard Sternbach and published by Holt, Rinehart & Winston (1972).

Not only do we use precise procedures in making the slides for the experiments, but we also control the amount of illumination occurring in the room in which the experiment takes place. All the slides are carefully checked after preparation for total brightness and dark-light contrast in the apparatus itself and in the actual experimental conditions. The methods we have developed for preparation of the picture slides also are applicable, with appropriate modification, to filmed material.

For the experiment itself there are certain procedural precautions which we follow. The order of the picture slides is one of them. We have found that the first picture a subject sees during an experiment will cause his pupil to dilate strongly. This reaction is to the novelty aspect of the situation. Therefore in order to keep the pupil responses to the crucial pictures from being contaminated by the novelty effect we add one or two irrelevant pictures which have been shown by our research to evoke little pupil response from subjects—dull landscapes, for example.

Two Russian researchers, E. N. Sokolov and A. E. Liberman, have both reported this novelty effect in the pupil dilation orienting reflex. Liberman has especially emphasized this, for he found that repeatedly giving the very same stimulus—such as sound or smell—within an experimental session will result in the pupillary dilation orienting response getting smaller and smaller. Furthermore, John J. Woodmansee of this country has noted that adaptation to the experiment will sometimes cause a decrease in the subjects' pupil size.

Another precaution which we observe in setting up our experiments is that we must be careful not to get the subject tired by showing him too many pictures since fatigue will cause the pupil to grow steadily smaller. The frequency and length of eye blinks also increase. When this happens it becomes very difficult to get enough measurements of the pupil during the period of exposure to the picture in question; thus we end up by not knowing how the subject did react after all. Therefore in order to prevent this from happening the maximum we ever use is 15 or 16 picture slides (with an equal number of control slides) and normally we use fewer than that number for a specific experimental session.

## PERCEPTION APPARATUS

Some years ago, before modern electronics, the noisy and cumbersome devices that were made and used to study the pupil often highly resembled the fabled Rube Goldberg inventions. Figure A1 is an example of these early pupil measure

**Figure A1**    This is a pupillographic apparatus devised by Otto Löwenstein, one of the foremost pupillographers in this century. Löwenstein was able to use this apparatus to record sequential pupil size changes cinematographically. As may readily be seen, the equipment and methods available in that era were highly cumbersome. Both eyes were photographed. Subjects wore a small ruler on their foreheads so that the actual pupil sizes could be determined from the photographic records. (Abb. 1, from O. Löwenstein, *Archiv für Psychiatrie und Nervenkrankheiten,* Band 82, s. 285–314, 1927.)

devices. Today, of course, things are much better. After our papers appeared quite a few apparatuses were developed which measure changes in pupil size. Of these, there are several commercial electronic apparatuses which are applicable for use in pupillometric investigations. They are all based on the use of infrared light for measuring pupil size.

The first is the Polymetric Wide Angle Recorder V-1166 (see Figure A2) developed by Polymetric Products Division of Itek Corporation, Lexington, Massachusetts (Mackworth, 1968). It is a versatile instrument and allows the use of pictorial and nonvisual material. Either white light or near-infrared red light can be used to illuminate the eye pupil. A small T.V. camera provides the means of showing the subject's eye on a closed circuit T.V. screen. An electronic device analyzes the signals from the pupil to determine the diameter, which is recorded on a polygraph.

Two pupil recording systems, Model 1021 and Model 830, are available from Whittaker Corporation, Space Sciences Division, Waltham, Massachusetts (see Figure A3). They are derived from the "T.V. Pupillometer" originally developed by Dr. Lawrence Stark (Asano and Stark, 1962; O'Neill and Stark, 1968). Like the apparatus we just now discussed, they use a closed circuit T.V. system. It

**Figure A2**   The pupil apparatus manufactured by Polymetric Products. (*Photo courtesy of Polymetric Products Division of Itek Corporation, Lexington, Massachusetts.*)

employs infrared light for illuminating the eye and a chart recorder for instant reading of data. The signal from the T.V. camera is modified by a signal processor and then the voltage is presented on the chart recording by means of pen markers, as representing the pupil diameter. Model 1021 not only records pupil size, but also determines the point of gaze of a subject during the viewing of visual material. We have recently used their latest equipment and found it to be very satisfactory.

Another machine, the BioLogic P-729, manufactured by BioLogic Instruments Inc., Ann Arbor, Michigan, consists of a television camera containing an infrared-sensitive vidicon, a television monitor, and solid state digital signal processing circuits. The scanning rate permits pupil diameter measurements to be made at rates as high as 30 or 60 per second.

Still another machine is the Iriscorder, manufactured by Hamamatsu Corporation, Lake Success, New York (see Figure A4). It utilizes an infrared light source, an electrostatic television camera, television monitor, and an oscillographic recorder (Ishikawa, Naito and Inaba, 1969). Pupil area rather than pupil diameter is measured. The manufacturers claim that .002 mm$^2$ area changes are detectable, and that 100 pupil area measurements can be made per second.

Two machines which can be used for pupillographic research are manufactured by Colorado Video, Incorporated, Boulder, Colorado. The first of these is the Video Target Diameter Analyser 611. The Analyser can be used with an inexpensive industrial television camera that has been modified so that its scanning yoke has been rotated 90 degrees. The video signal from this camera is processed by the Analyser to generate dc voltage which is directly proportional to the size of the pupil. The output from the Analyser can be fed to any appropriate indicating device such as a digital voltmeter or chart recorder. The other machine is the Video Analyser Model 302. It can also be used with a television camera to analyze video signals from the eye.

Our own equipment was developed for the purpose of recording pupil size while a subject is looking at specific pictures presented by means of a slide or movie projector. Its use with a movie projector is a relatively new area of investigation. Our equipment will also permit us to determine which portion of the stimulus is being looked at during each half second of the viewing.

Figure A5 depicts the portable perception apparatus which is used in our pupillometric research. On the top is a handle for carrying it around. At the left is the viewing aperture through which the subject looks to see the pictures. To the right, in back of the apparatus, is the slide projector which projects the pictures from the slides on the back of the apparatus. On the side of the apparatus is a mounted 16 mm Bolex Rex II movie camera which records the subjects' pupils on infrared film at the rate of two pictures per second. We use infrared film because it lets us use brown- and black-eyed subjects whose pupils would otherwise be very difficult to see on the film record because of lack of contrast between the iris and pupil in ordinary white light. This way, with infrared film, we can get excellent records from subjects of any eye color.

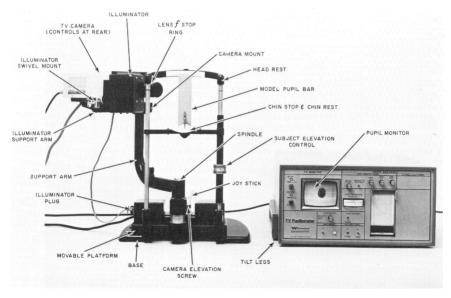

**Figure A3**  Model 1021 pupil apparatus available from Whittaker Corporation. (*Photo courtesy of Whittaker Corporation, Space Sciences Division, Waltham, Massachusetts.*)

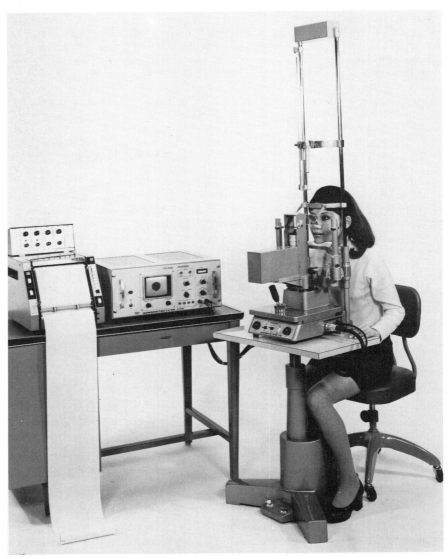

**Figure A4**  The Iriscorder manufactured by Hamamatsu Corporation for pupil studies. (*Photo courtesy of Hamamatsu Corporation, Lake Success, New York.*)

Figure A6 shows a schematic diagram of the inside of the pupil recording apparatus. There, the basic principles used in the presentation of pictures and the recording of the pupil responses to the pictures may be seen. The precise dimensions of the components of the apparatus and a description of the control switches and how the movie camera and slide projector are operated is in the *Handbook of Psychophysiology,* Chapter 12, to which we referred earlier.

Only one eye needs to be photographed since we have found that when both eyes are photographed simultaneously the pupillary behavior changes of the two eyes usually follow each other perfectly. As we have noted in Chapter 3, P. R. A. May found in 1948, that marked differences in the size of the two eye pupils are relatively rare in the nonpsychiatric population. The same size pupil in both eyes in normal people has also been observed by other researchers who have used flashes of light or other kinds of sensations.

In 1970, John Varni and Ernest Clark of the University of Washington at Seattle reported very interesting findings regarding the physiological adaptation responses to stress in persons whose left-right pupil sizes are different despite equal illumination conditions for both eyes. Since this research was carried out 20 years after May's, much smaller differences in pupil size may be involved due to the greater precision and sophistication of today's measuring instruments.

What Varni and Clark found was that such people, called *anisocorics,* not only evidenced greater variability than nonanisocorics in heartbeat rate, but

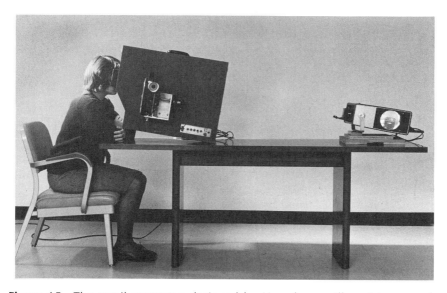

**Figure A5**   The pupil apparatus designed by Hess for pupillometric research, seen from the side. The subject's head is positioned onto the face piece opening in the front. The movie camera that photographs the eye pupil is shown on the side of the apparatus. The slide projector that projects the slides on the viewing screen is shown to the rear, on the right hand side of the photo.

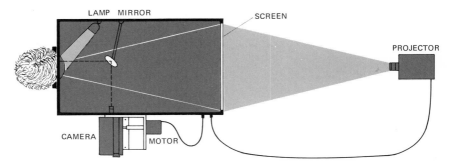

**Figure A6** Schematic diagram of the Hess pupil apparatus. The essential components are shown in relation to each other. A red lamp is used to illuminate the eye. The mirror reflects the image of the eye to the Bolex II movie camera, which records the pupil size changes on infrared film, usually at the rate of two frames per second. The mirror is placed below the eye level so that there is no obstruction of the viewing screen. A timer within the pupil apparatus causes the projector to advance to successive slides every ten seconds. (From Hess, E. H., Attitude and pupil size. *Scientific American*, **212**, No. 4, 46–54 (1965). Copyright © 1965 by Scientific American, Inc. All rights reserved.)

also better withstood stress situations. For example, if the skin were scratched (without breaking the skin) the anisocorics' skin reddened faster at the site of the irritation than did the nonanisocorics'. Their mouth and finger temperatures showed smaller drops in response to cold and other stress situations than did those for the nonanisocorics. Also, their heartbeat rates were on the average lower in nonstress situations and remained lower in stress situations than the nonanisocorics.

These physiological differences in anisocorics are of interest to us in that it has been found that there appear to be personality differences associated with whether or not a person tends to give large or small pupil responses in comparison with other people, as we have discussed in Chapter 12. Varni and Clark's findings should, we feel, be further explored, not only on the physiological level but also on the psychological level.

## TESTING OF SUBJECTS

Before the subject is brought into the experimental room with the apparatus in it, the apparatus is readied so that the first control slide is projected on the screen and the timer for the slide projection is set to show each control and picture slide for ten seconds. The camera has been loaded with film and connected to the slide projector timer. A frame counter is also attached to the camera so as to keep track of the film record in relation to the picture and control slides. A red bulb used for illuminating the eye with red light within the apparatus is turned on.

The subject is then brought to the apparatus and given instructions as follows: "We would like to have you place your head so that you can comfortably see the numbers which are on this slide we are showing. In a few moments we will show you a number of pictures. Each picture will be preceded by a control slide just like this one. Please look at each control slide when it appears by following the numbers 1, 2, 3, 4, and 5. The experimenter will pace you at first, and then you will follow the same procedure for each control slide. When the pictures come on, you can, of course, look where you please. Do not look into the light or at the wall of the apparatus, etc. The entire run will take only a few minutes, so that even if you are not too comfortable after the session begins, please try to keep your head in the exact position into which the experimenter has helped you to place it." This is the extent to which instructions are given to our subjects.

After the subject places his head into the viewing aperture, with help from the experimenter if necessary, a focusing light is turned on and the subject is asked to look steadily at the numeral "5" in the center of the screen while the focusing of the camera is accomplished. This normally takes only a few seconds, after which the focusing light inside the apparatus is turned off. The actual experiment is begun five to ten seconds later to adapt the subject's eyes to the illumination inside the apparatus.

After the subject is tested, several feet of film are run on the movie camera to separate the film records of successive subjects on the same reel of film. When a reel of film has been used up it is carefully identified with the subjects' numbers, date, and a description of the experimental run so that there will be no mix-up when the film is processed and analyzed.

## PUPIL MEASUREMENT

Measuring the film records involves projecting each frame of the movie film and measuring the pupil diameter. These pupil diameters are recorded on a tabulation sheet. The average (arithmetical mean) size of the pupil diameter for the twenty frames taken during the ten seconds that a control slide was projected is the basis upon which the change in pupil diameter during the ten-second viewing of the picture shown immediately after is judged. The average size of the pupil diameter for the twenty frames taken during the projection of the picture slide is subtracted from the average control size and the difference is computed as a positive or negative per cent of the original pupil diameter. Not all twenty slides of control and picture responses, of course, may be measurable due to blinking or very rapid eye movement. Since we have taken numerous steps to make sure that brightness or contrast factors do not play a role in the pupil size changes we know that the changes we do obtain actually are indicators of the subjects' mental or emotional responses to the pictures.

The control slides also control for additional factors, such as accommodation, which can affect pupil size. Furthermore, the ten-second viewing intervals of both control and picture slides which have the same illumination level permit the constantly fluctuating pupil size (described as stochastic "pupil noise" by Lawrence Stark in 1969) to be as small as possible a factor in pupil size since 15–20 frames are available for calculations. Finally, delays in dilation and contraction sequences, such as have been described by Gad Hakerem and Arnold Lidsky, do not materially affect the determination of pupillary reaction to picture slides since these delays are generally less than half a second in duration.

The frame-by-frame measurement of the pupil is carried out with the aid of a stop frame movie projector. We use a Perceptoscope, manufactured by Perceptual Development Laboratories, Big Spring, Texas. Other single-frame projectors on the market are also suitable for the purpose. The Perceptoscope is placed on the floor about one yard away from a table which is at the same height as a desk top. This table has a mirror placed under it that throws the image from the Perceptoscope onto a piece of frosted glass set in a hole in the table. This results in enlarging the picture of the pupil which is then measured in millimeters with a transparent ruler. Most of the pupil diameters fall within 30 to 80 millimeters in size, allowing an accuracy of 96 to 99 per cent in measurement.

We also have developed an alternative method of measuring pupil size by means of using a photocell and recording the changes in pupil area electronically. These readings are then changed into pupil diameter mathematically.

We can also analyze the movements of the eye on the film record so as to determine precisely what the subject is looking at during any given moment of exposure to the pictures. The film negative is first projected on a photograph of the control slide and the beam that passes through the image of the pupil is calibrated with the numerals on the control slide. This can be done because, as was mentioned above, each subject looks at the numerals of each control slide in a paced sequence. Then when the pupil responses to a picture slide are projected upon a photograph of the picture slide the beam passing through the image of the pupil will fall upon the precise spot that the subject had been looking at during each frame of the film record.

While we have been discussing in detail our procedure for studying pupil responses to pictures, our apparatus certainly can also be used for situations where no pictures are involved. For example, we have had subjects look steadily at an "x" or a "5" in the center of a control slide while they perform arithmetic problems in their heads, spell, make anagrams, listen to music or other sounds, smell various odors, take puffs from various brands of cigarettes, sip flavored beverages, or receive touch, heat, or cold sensations.

Findings so far obtained in these "nonvisual" situations have been extremely interesting and highly suggestive of the great value and use of pupillometrics;

especially since the pupil size changes observed in these situations occur without any illumination changes that could affect the pupil. These findings, in addition to the ones obtained with visual material, indicate to us that the field of pupillometrics has hardly been touched.

# Bibliography

ASANO, S., and STARK, L. Pupillometry. *M.I.T. Quarterly Progress Reports in Electronics*, **66,** 404 (1962).

ATWOOD, ROBERT W., and HOWELL, ROBERT J. Pupillometric and personality test score differences of pedophiliacs and normals. *Psychonomic Science*, **22,** 115–116 (1971).

BARLOW, JERRY DEAN. Pupillary size as an index of preference in political candidates. *Perceptual and Motor Skills*, **28,** 587–590 (1969).

BEATTY, JACKSON, and KAHNEMAN, DANIEL. Pupillary changes in two memory tasks. *Psychonomic Science*, **5,** 371–372 (1966).

BECK, BENJAMIN B. The effect of auditory stimulation on the photopupil reflex response. Unpublished doctoral dissertation at The University of Chicago, 1967.

BERNICK, NILES. The development of children's preferences for social objects as evidenced by their pupil responses. Unpublished doctoral thesis at The University of Chicago, 1966.

BERNICK, NILES, KLING, ARTHUR, and BOROWITZ, GENE. Physiologic differentiation of sexual arousal and anxiety. *Psychosomatic Medicine*, **33,** 341–352 (1971).

BIRREN, J. E., CASPERSON, R. C., and BOTWINICK, J. Age changes in pupil size. *Journal of Gerontology*, **5,** 216–221 (1950).

BOERSMA, FREDERIC, WILTON, KERI, BARHAM, RICHARD, and MUIR, WALTER. Effects of arithmetic problem difficulty on pupillary dilation in normals and educable retardates. *Journal of Experimental Child Psychology*, **9,** 142–155 (1970).

BORTEL, F. J. VAN. Commercial applications of pupillometrics. In: F. M. Bass, C. W. King, and E. A. Pessemier (Eds.), *Applications of the Sciences in Marketing Management*, pp. 439–453. New York: Wiley, 1968.

BRADSHAW, JOHN L. Pupil size as a measure of arousal during information processing. *Nature*, **216,** 515–516 (1967).

233

BRADSHAW, JOHN L. Load and pupillary changes in continuous processing tasks. *British Journal of Psychology*, **59**, 265–271 (1968).

BRADSHAW, JOHN L. Background light intensity and the pupillary response in a reaction time task. *Psychonomic Science*, **14**, 271–272 (1969).

BRADSHAW, JOHN L. Pupil size and drug state in a reaction time task. *Psychonomic Science*, **18**, 112–113 (1970).

BUMKE, OSWALD. *Die Pupillenstörungen, Bei Geistes- und Nerven-krankheiten* (Physiologie und Pathologie der Irisbewegungen). Jena: Fischer, 1911.

BYRNE, DONN. The repression-sensitization scale: Rationale, reliability, and validity. *Journal of Personality*, **29**, 334–349 (1961).

CANN, MICHAEL A. An investigation of a component of parental behavior in humans. Unpublished paper submitted to E. Hess of the Department of Psychology in candidacy for the degree of Master of Arts, Committee on Human Development, The University of Chicago, Chicago, Illinois, June 1953.

CHAPMAN, LOREN J., CHAPMAN, JEAN P., and BRELJE, TERRY. Influences of the experimenter on pupillary dilation to sexually provocative pictures. *Journal of Abnormal Psychology*, **74**, 396–400 (1969).

CLARK, WILLIAM RUSSELL. A pupillographic study of short-term memory search. *Dissertation Abstracts International*, **31**, 6279B-6280B (1970).

CLARK, WILLIAM RUSSELL, and JOHNSON, DAVID A. Effects of instructional set on pupillary responses during a short-term memory task. *Journal of Experimental Psychology*, **85**, 315–317 (1970).

COLLINS, BARRY E., ELLSWORTH, PHOEBE C., and HELMREICH, ROBERT L. Correlations between pupil size and the semantic differential: An experimental paradigm and pilot study. *Psychonomic Science*, **9**, 627–628 (1967).

COLMAN, FRANK D., and PAIVIO, ALLAN. Pupillary response and galvanic skin response during an imagery task. *Psychonomic Science*, **16**, 296–297 (1969).

COLMAN, FRANK D., and PAIVIO, ALLAN. Pupillary dilation and mediation processes during paired-associate learning. *Canadian Journal of Psychology*, **24**, 261–270 (1970).

COSS, RICHARD G. *Mood Provoking Visual Stimuli: Their Origins and Applications.* Los Angeles: Industrial Design Graduate Program, University of California, 1965.

COVERDALE, HERBERT L. Pupillary response, connotative meaning and personality. *Dissertation Abstracts International*, **31**, 5045B (1970).

CROUGH, DAVID GUY. An investigation of differential pupillary response between groups differing in reasoning ability. *Dissertation Abstracts International*, **32**, 1870B (1971).

DARWIN, CHARLES. *The Expression of the Emotions in Man and Animals.* London: Murray, 1872.

ELSHTAIN, ERROL L., and SCHAEFER, THEODORE, JR. Effects of storage load and word frequency on pupillary responses during short-term memory. *Psychonomic Science*, **12**, 143–144 (1968).

EYSENCK, H. J. *The Biological Basis of Personality.* Springfield, Illinois: C. C. Thomas, 1967.

EYSENCK, H. J. and EYSENCK, SYBIL B. G. On the unitary nature of extraversion. *Acta Psychologica*, **26,** 383–390 (1967).

EYSENCK, SYBIL B. G. and EYSENCK, H. J. Physiological reactivity to sensory stimulation as a measure of personality. *Psychological Reports*, **20,** 45–46 (1967).

EYSENCK, SYBIL B. G. and EYSENCK, H. J. Salivary response to lemon juice as a measure of introversion. *Perceptual and Motor Skills*, **24,** 1047–1053 (1967).

FITZGERALD, HIRAM E. Autonomic pupillary reflex activity during early infancy and its relation to social and nonsocial visual stimuli. *Journal of Experimental Child Psychology*, **6,** 470–482 (1968).

FOA, PIO, and SCHIFF, J. MORITZ (MAURIZIO). La pupilla come estesiometro. *Imparziale*, **14,** 617–626, 649–655, 691–702 (1874).

FONTANA, FELICE F. *Sui moti dell'iride.* Lucca: J. Giusti, 1765.

FRANCIS, R. D. Neuroticism and optical pupil changes in response to auditory stimuli. *British Journal of Social and Clinical Psychology*, **8,** 344–349 (1969).

FRANCIS, R. D., and KELLY, M. R. An investigation of the relationship between word stimuli and optical pupil size. *Australian Journal of Psychology*, **21,** 117–125 (1969).

FREDERICKS, RICHARD S. Repression-sensitization and pupillary response to pleasant and unpleasant stimuli. *Dissertation Abstracts International*, **31,** 2982B (1970).

FREDERICKS, RICHARD S., and GROVES, MARION H. Pupil changes and stimulus pleasantness. *Proceedings of the Annual Convention of the American Psychological Association*, **6,** 371–372 (1971).

GANG, KENNETH. Psychosomatic factors in the control of pupillary movement. *Journal of Clinical Psychopathology and Psychotherapy*, **6,** 461–472 (1945).

GOLDWATER, BRAM C. Psychological significance of pupillary movements. *Psychological Bulletin*, **77,** 340–355 (1972).

GOOD, LAWRENCE R., and LEVIN, RICHARD H. Pupillary responses of repressors and sensitizers to sexual and aversive stimuli. *Perceptual and Motor Skills*, **30,** 631–634 (1970).

GREEN, DANIEL G., and MAASEIDVAAG, FRODE. Closed-circuit television pupillometer. *Journal of the Optical Society of America*, **57,** 830–833 (1967).

GUMP, RICHARD. *Jade: Stone of Heaven.* New York: Doubleday, 1962.

HAHN, HELMUT, KUCKULIES, GÜNTER, and TAEGER, HARALD. Eine systematische Üntersuchung der Geschmacksschwellen: I. *Zeitschrift für Sinnesphysiologie*, **67,** 259–306 (1938).

HAKEREM, GAD, and LIDSKY, ARNOLD. Pupillary reactions to sequences of light and variable dark impulses. *Annals of the New York Academy of Sciences*, **156** (2), 951–958 (1969).

HAKEREM, GAD, and SUTTON, SAMUEL. Pupillary response at visual threshold. *Nature*, **212,** 485–486 (1966).

HEINRICH, W. Die Aufmerksamkeit und die Funktion der Sinnesorgane. *Zeitschrift für Psychologie und Physiologie der Sinnesorgane*, **9,** 342–388 (1896).

HESS, ECKHARD H. Some relationships between pupillary activity and mental activity. Paper presented at American Psychological Association Meeting, September, 1964.

HESS, ECKHARD H. Attitude and pupil size. *Scientific American*, No. 4, 46–54 (1965).

HESS, ECKHARD H. Pupillometrics. In: F. M. Bass, C. W. King, and E. A. Pessemier (Eds.), *Applications of the Sciences in Marketing Management*, p. 431–438. New York: Wiley, 1968.

HESS, ECKHARD H. Pupillometrics: A method of studying mental, emotional, and sensory processes. In: N. Greenfield, and R. Sternbach (Eds.), *Handbook of Psychophysiology*, Chapter 12, pp. 491–531. New York: Holt, Rinehart and Winston, 1972.

HESS, ECKHARD H., and POLT, JAMES M. Pupil size as related to interest value of visual stimuli. *Science*, **132**, 349–350 (1960).

HESS, ECKHARD H., and POLT, JAMES M. Pupil size in relation to mental activity during simple problem-solving. *Science*, **143**, 1190–1192 (1964).

HESS, ECKHARD H., and POLT, JAMES M. Changes in pupil size as a measure of taste difference. *Perceptual and Motor Skills*, **23**, 451–455 (1966).

HESS, ECKHARD H., and POLT, JAMES M. Reply to "critique of a pupillary response experiment" by Roger P. Dooley and Donald J. Lehr. *Perceptual and Motor Skills*, **25**, 659–660 (1967).

HESS, ECKHARD H., SELTZER, ALLAN L., and SHLIEN, JOHN M. Pupil response of hetero- and homosexual males to pictures of men and women: A pilot study. *Journal of Abnormal Psychology*, **70**, 165–168 (1965).

HICKS, ROBERT A., REANEY, TOM, and HILL, LYNN. Effects of pupil size and facial angle on preference for photographs of a young woman. *Perceptual and Motor Skills*, **24**, 388–390 (1967).

HUTT, LEMLY D. Selective attention: The relationship between pupil size and recognition threshold. *Dissertation Abstracts*, **29**, 388–389B (1968).

HUTT, LEMLY D., and ANDERSON, J. The relationship between pupil size and recognition threshold. *Psychonomic Science*, **9**, 477–478 (1967).

ISHIKAWA, SATOSHI, NAITO, MAKOTO, and INABA, KOJI. A new videopupillography. Department of Opthalmology, School of Medicine, University of Tokyo. 7-3-1 Hong, Bunkyo-ku, Tokyo, Japan. Undated, but probably 1969.

JOHNSON, DAVID A. Pupillary responses during a short-term memory task: Cognitive processing, arousal, or both? *Journal of Experimental Psychology*, **90**, 313–318 (1971).

JONES, QUANA R., and MOYEL, ISAIAH S. The influence of iris color and pupil size on expressed affect. *Psychonomic Science*, **22**, 126–127 (1971).

KAHNEMAN, DANIEL. Construct validity of the pupil response. Paper presented at Pupil Symposium, APA Convention, Washington, D. C., 1967.

KAHNEMAN, DANIEL, and BEATTY, JACKSON. Pupil diameter and load on memory. *Science*, **154**, 1583–1585 (1966).

KAHNEMAN, DANIEL, and BEATTY, JACKSON. Pupillary responses in a pitch-discrimination task. *Perception and Psychophysics*, **2**, 101–105 (1967).

KAHNEMAN, DANIEL, and PEAVLER, W. SCOTT. Incentive effects and pupillary changes in association learning. *Journal of Experimental Psychology*, **79,** 312–318 (1969).

KAHNEMAN, DANIEL, PEAVLER, W. SCOTT, and ONUSKA, L. Effects of verbalization and incentive on the pupil response to mental activity. *Canadian Journal of Psychology*, **22,** 186–196 (1968).

KENNEDY, OWEN A. Pupillometrics as an aid in the assessment of motivation, impact of treatment and prognosis of chronic alcoholics. *Dissertation Abstracts International*, **32,** 1214B-1215B (1971).

KLEIN, R., and EARLY, D. F. Observations on the electrically produced epileptic convulsion. Part II. Pupillary phenomena in normal and pathological pupils. *Journal of Mental Science*, **94,** 805–808 (1948).

KRUEGER, LAWRENCE M. Voluntary control of pupillary responses to visual stimuli. *Dissertation Abstracts*, **28,** 2644B (1967).

KRUGMAN, HERBERT E. Some applications of pupil measurement. *Journal of Marketing Research*, **1,** 15–19 (November, 1964).

KRUGMAN, HERBERT E. Pupil measurement at Marplan. *The Brewer's Digest*, 26–28 (November, 1964).

KRUGMAN, HERBERT E. A comparison of physical and verbal responses to television commercials. *The Public Opinion Quarterly*, **29,** 323–325 (1965).

KRUGMAN, HERBERT E. Processes underlying exposure to advertising. *American Psychologist*, **23,** 245–253 (1968).

KUMNICK, L. S. Pupillary psychosensory restitution and aging. *Journal of the Optical Society of America*, **44,** 735–741 (1954).

KUMNICK, L. S. Aging and pupillary response to light and sound stimuli. *Journal of Gerontology*, **11,** 38–45 (1956).

KUMNICK, L. S. Aging and the efficiency of the pupillary mechanism. *Journal of Gerontology*, **11,** 160–164 (1956).

LACK, D. The behavior of the robin. II. *Proceedings of the Zoological Society of London*, **109,** 200–219 (1939).

LANGE, ANDERS L. Pupillutvidgning och perception. Ett humanetologiskt experiment. Unpublished manuscript, February, 1964.

LEVINE, ALEXANDER, and SCHILDER, PAUL. The catatonic pupil. *Journal of Nervous and Mental Disease*, **96,** 1–12 (1942).

LIBERMAN, A. E. Some new data on the pupillary component in man. In: L. G. Voronin, *et al.* (Eds.), *Orienting Reflex and Exploratory Behavior*, pp. 187–194. Translated by V. Shmelev and K. Hanes. Edited by D. B. Lindsley. Washington, D. C.: American Institute of Biological Sciences, 1965.

LOEWENFELD, IRENE E. Pupil size. *Survey of Ophthalmology*, **11,** 291–294 (1966).

LORENS, STANLEY, and DARROW, CHESTER. Eye movements, EEG, GSR, and EKG during mental multiplication. *Electroencephalography and Clinical Neurophysiology*, **14,** 739–746 (1962).

LORENZ, KONRAD Z. Die angeborenen Formen möglicher Erfahrung. *Zeitschrift für Tierpsychologie*, **5,** 235–409 (1943).

LÖWENSTEIN, OTTO. Experimentelle Beiträge zur Lehre von den katatonischen Pupillenveränderungen. *Monatsschrift für Psychiatrie und Neurologie*, **47,** 194–215 (1920).

LÖWENSTEIN, OTTO. Über die Variationsbreite des Lichtreflexes und der Psychoreflexe der Pupillen. *Archiv für Psychiatrie und Nervenkrankheiten*, **82,** 285–314 (1927).

LÖWENSTEIN, OTTO,, and LOEWENFELD, IRENE E. Role of sympathetic and parasympathetic systems in reflex dilatation of the pupil. *AMA Archives of Neurology and Psychiatry*, **64,** 313–340 (1950).

LÖWENSTEIN, OTTO, and WESTPHAL, ALEXANDER. *Experimentelle und klinische Studien zur Physiologie der Pupillenbewegungen* (Mit bes. Berücks d. Schizophrenie). Berlin: Karger, 1933.

McLEAN, JAMES DICKSON. Eye to eye: The social significance of the pupil. Unpublished doctoral dissertation, The University of Chicago, 1974.

MACHOTKA, PAVEL. Defensive style and esthetic distortion. *Journal of Personality*, **35,** 600–621 (1967).

MACKWORTH, NORMAN H. The wide-angle reflection eye camera for visual choice and pupil size. *Perception and Psychophysics*, **3,** 32–34 (1968).

MAY, P. R. A. Pupillary abnormalities in schizophrenia and during muscular effort. *Journal of Mental Science*, **94,** 89–98 (1948).

MEYER, E. Pupillenstörungen bei Dementia praecox. *Berliner Klinische Wochenschrift*, **47,** 1813–1815 (1910).

NUNNALLY, JUM C. Pupillary response in anticipation of emotion-provoking events. Paper presented at Pupil Symposium, APA Convention, Washington, D. C., 1967.

NUNNALLY, JUM C., KNOTT, PAUL D., DUCHNOWSKI, ALBERT, and PARKER, RONALD. Pupillary response as a general measure of activation. *Perception and Psychophysics*, **2,** 149–155 (1967).

O'NEILL, W. D., and STARK, L. Triple-function ocular monitor. *Journal of the Optical Society of America*, **58,** 570 (1968).

PAIVIO, ALLAN, and SIMPSON, HERB M. Magnitude and latency of the pupillary response during an imagery task as a function of stimulus abstractness and imagery ability. *Psychonomic Science*, **12,** 45–46 (1968).

PARKER, RONALD K., and MOGYOROSY, ROBERT S. Pupillary response to induced muscular tension. Paper presented at Pupil Symposium, APA Convention, Washington, D. C., 1967.

PAYNE, DONALD T., PARRY, MARY ELLEN, and HARASYMIW, STEFAN J. Percentage of pupillary dilation as a measure of item difficulty. *Perception and Psychophysics*, **4,** 139–143 (1968).

PEAVLER, W. SCOTT. Attention, processing load, and pupil size. *Dissertation Abstracts International*, **30,** 1929B (1969).

PEAVLER, W. SCOTT, and McLAUGHLIN, JOHN P. The question of stimulus content and pupil size. *Psychonomic Science*, **8,** 505–506 (1967).

POLT, JAMES M. Effect of threat of shock on pupillary response in a problem solving situation. *Perceptual and Motor Skills*, **31,** 587–593 (1970).

POLT, JAMES M., and HESS, ECKHARD H. Changes in pupil size to visually presented words. *Psychonomic Science*, **12,** 389–390 (1968).

PRATT, ROBIN W. Cognitive processing of uncertainty: Its effects on pupillary dilation and preference ratings. *Perception and Psychophysics,* **8,** 193–198 (1970).

REDLICH, EMIL. Zur Characteristik der reflektorische Pupillenstarre bei der progressive Paralyse. *Neurologische Zentralblatt,* **11,** 307–312 (1892).

REDLICH, EMIL. *Die Pathologie der tabischen Hinterstrangserkrankung.* Jena: G. Fischer, 1897.

REDLICH, EMIL. Kräftige und andauerende Muskelkontraktion ausgelösten Erweiterung der Pupille. *Zeitschrift für Augenheilkunde,* **19,** 171–172 (1908).

REDLICH, EMIL. Ueber ein eigenartiges Pupillenphänomen; zugleich ein Beitrag zur Frage der hysterischen Pupillenstarre. *Deutsche medizinische Wochenschrift,* **34,** 313–315 (1908).

REICHMANN, FRIEDA. Ueber Pupillenstörungen bei Dementia Praecox. *Archiv für Psychiatrie und Nervenkrankheiten,* **53,** 302–321 (1914).

ROUBINOVITCH, JACQUES. Du reflexe ideo-moteur de la pupille. *Revue Neurologique,* **8,** 740–741 (1900).

ROUBINOVITCH, JACQUES. Des variations du diamètre pupillaire en rapport avec l'effort intellectuel. *IVᴱ Congrès International de Psychologie (1900),* pp. 522–523. Compte rendu des seances et textes des mémoires, publiés par les soins du docteur Pierre Janet. Paris: F. Alcan, 1901.

RUBIN, LEONARD S., BARBERO, GIULIO J., CHERNIK, WARREN S., and SIBINGA, MAARTEN S. Pupillary reactivity as a measure of autonomic balance in cystic fibrosis. *Journal of Pediatrics,* **63,** 1120–1129 (1963).

SCHAEFER, THEODORE, JR., FERGUSON, J. BRINTON, KLEIN, JOSEPH A., and RAWSON, EDWARD B. Pupillary responses during mental activities. *Psychonomic Science,* **12,** 137–138 (1968).

SCHIFF, J. MORITZ (MAURICE). *La pupille considerée comme esthésiomètre.* Tr. de l'italien par Dr. R. Guichard de Choisity. Paris: J.-B. Baillière, 1875.

SCHIFF, J. MORITZ (MAURICE), and FOA, PIO. La pupille considerée comme esthésiomètre. Tr. de l'italien par le Dr. de Choisity. *Marseille médical,* **2,** 736–741 (1874).

SCHWEIKERT, JOHN W. Pupillometrics: A pilot study to appraise its potential as a non-verbal instrument to evaluate student attitudes. *Dissertation Abstracts International,* **30,** 2937B (1969).

SELTZER, ALLAN L. Hypnosis and pupil response. Unpublished doctoral dissertation at The University of Chicago, 1969.

SHEFLIN, JOSEPH A. An application of Hess' pupillometric procedure to a psychiatric population: An approach utilizing sexual stimuli. *Dissertation Abstracts International,* **30,** 1907B (1969).

SHER, MONROE ALLEN. Pupillary dilation during recall and following interruption of recall. *Dissertation Abstracts International,* **31,** 4372B (1971).

SILBERKUHL, W. Untersuchungen über die physiologische Pupillenweite. *Albrecht von Graefe's Archiv für Ophthalmologie,* **42,** 179–187 (1896).

SIMMS, THOMAS M. Pupillary response of male and female subjects to pupillary difference in male and female picture stimuli. *Perception and Psychophysics,* **2,** 553–555 (1967).

SIMPSON, HERB M., and CLIMAN, M. H. Pupillary and electromyographic changes during an imagery task. *Psychophysiology,* **8,** 483–490 (1971).

SIMPSON, HERB M., and HALE, SHIRLEY M. Pupillary changes during a decision making task. *Perceptual and Motor Skills,* **29,** 495–498 (1969).

SIMPSON, HERB M., and MOLLOY, FIONA M. Effects of audience anxiety on pupil size. *Psychophysiology,* **8,** 491–496 (1971).

SIMPSON, HERB M., MOLLOY, FIONA M., HALE, SHIRLEY M., and CLIMAN, M. H. Latency and magnitude of the pupillary response during an imagery task. *Psychonomic Science,* **13,** 293–294 (1968).

SIMPSON, HERB M., and PAIVIO, ALLAN. Effects on pupil size of manual and verbal indicators of cognitive task fulfillment. *Perception and Psychophysics,* **3,** 185–190 (1968).

SOKOLOV, E. N. The orienting reflex, its structure and mechanisms. In: L. G. Voronin, *et al.* (Eds.), *Orienting Reflex and Exploratory Behavior,* pp. 141–151. Translated by V. Shmelev and K. Hanes. Edited by D. B. Lindsley. Washington, D. C.: American Institute of Biological Sciences, 1965.

*SPONSOR,* ". . . in the eye of the beholder." December 28, 1964.

STARK, LAWRENCE. Pupillary control system: Its nonlinear adaptive and stochastic engineering design characteristics. *Federation Proceedings,* **28,** 52–64 (1969).

STASS, JOHN W., and WILLIS, FRANK N., JR. Eye contact, pupil dilation, and personal preference. *Psychonomic Science,* **7,** 375–376 (1967).

STEWART, R. W., and JENSEN, D. D. GSR, pupillary dilation, and response latency to words differing in entropy. Paper presented at Midwest Psychological Association meeting, Chicago, 1966.

STRELTSOVA, N. I. The influence of some physiological and pharmacological factors on the pupillary orienting reflex. In: L. G. Voronin, *et al.* (Eds.), *Orienting Reflex and Exploratory Behavior,* pp. 399–406. Translated by V. Shmelev and K. Hanes. Edited by D. B. Lindsley. Washington, D. C.: American Institute of Biological Sciences, 1965.

TANCK, ROLAND H., and ROBBINS, PAUL R. Pupillary reactions to sexual, aggressive, and other stimuli as a function of personality. *Journal of Projective Techniques and Personality Assessment,* **34,** 277–282 (1970).

VACCHIANO, RALPH B., STRAUSS, PAUL S., RYAN, SHARON, and HOCHMAN, LEONARD. Pupillary response to value-linked words. *Perceptual and Motor Skills,* **27,** 207–210 (1968).

VARNI, JOHN G., and CLARK, R. ERNEST. Psychophysiological correlates of anisocoria. *Journal of Psychosomatic Research,* **14,** 195–201 (1970).

WATSON, JAMES D. *The Double Helix.* New York: Atheneum, 1968.

WESTPHAL, ALEXANDER. Ueber ein im katatonischen stupor beobachtetes Pupillenphänomen sowie Bemerkungen über die Pupillenstarre bei Hysterie. *Deutsche medizinische Wochenschrift,* **33,** 1080–1084 (1907).

WESTPHAL, CARL F. Ueber ein Pupillenphänomen in der Chloroformnarkose. *Virchows Archiv,* **27,** 409–412 (1863).

WIKLER, ABRAHAM, ROSENBERG, DAVID E., HAWTHORNE, JIMMIE D., and CASSIDY, THOMAS M. Age and effect of LSD-25 on pupil size and kneejerk threshold. *Psychopharmacologia,* **7,** 44–56 (1965).

WOODMANSEE, JOHN J. Methodological problems in pupillographic experiments. Paper presented at American Psychological Association meeting, New York, 1966.

WOODMANSEE, JOHN J. The pupil response as a measure of social attitudes. In: Gene Summers (Ed.), *Attitude Measurement*, pp. 514–533. New York: Rand McNally, 1970.

Faces into which pupils can be drawn. To be your own experimenter ask someone to draw the appropriately sized pupils into each of the two faces on opposite pages. Give him a pencil and see what happens.

# Index